Our World and the Universe Around It

PART I | THE UNIVERSE

OUR WORLD

and the Universe Around It

PART I   THE UNIVERSE

ORIGINAL TEXT IN ITALIAN BY Ginestra Amaldi

FREELY ADAPTED AND EXPANDED BY Norman Rudnick

PICTURE COMMENTARIES BY NORMAN RUDNICK

ABRADALE PRESS / *Publishers* / *New York*

500
A 4820
pt. 1

Library of Congress Catalog Card Number: 66-12316

Designed by Howard Morris

PRINTED AND BOUND IN ITALY

Foreword

As MAN'S KNOWLEDGE of the universe around him has expanded, his relationship to it has become at once more comprehensive and complex. During the past sixty years, science has advanced at a greater rate than in all previous recorded history. Less than 150 years ago, man believed he could not survive a speed of thirty-five miles per hour, yet today scientists predict spacecraft that will carry him at the speed of light. For thousands of years man sought to discover his origins, but only in the past one hundred years has he advanced the theory of evolution and begun to experiment with the basic chemical building blocks of life itself. So great have been these advances that the body of scientific knowledge is constantly changing, exploding yesterday's theories and expounding new ones based on today's discoveries. As we unlocked the secret of the atom, thereby opening another door to the universe, we entered an age in which science is the concern of every man. However, the accumulation of knowledge available to us has become so overwhelming and so subject to dynamic change that even our understanding of the basic principles is constantly undergoing revision.

This book attempts to explain, as clearly as possible, the most current scientific theories and achievements in astronomy, space exploration, chemistry, physics, geology, and biology. Yet, even as you read this Foreword, new theories are replacing those in many parts of the book, and new "truths"--no doubt to be replaced by others--will take their place. Therefore, we have tried, right up to press time, to include the most up-to-date material available. Wherever possible, we have used actual photographs of new and interesting subjects to supplement and enrich the text, and provide instructive and stimulating visual aids. Our aim has been to provide the reader, as far as possible, with an understanding of modern science.

Part I deals with the origin and nature of the universe: the various theories concerning its beginnings, its composition, size and motion. There is also a survey of current scentific attitudes and conclusions about the physical universe and its properties; and finally, man's exploration of space. The latest contributions to space and planetary science—close-up photographs taken from spacecraft—are part of special sections dealing with our first steps into space.

Part II concerns our own planet; ancient and current theories of the formation of the earth—mountain building, volcanoes, glaciation, and erosion. The earth is seen as the home of life as we know it, through evidence obtained from rocks, fossils, and the theories of natural selection, adaptation, and mutation. Man is placed in the vast continuum of life on earth and is seen as a link in the great chain of creation —a part of a vast and relentless force.

Part III explores the fields of physics and chemistry, energy and the structure of matter, tracing the achievements of modern science through its leaders and their greatest contributions. The mysteries of atoms, molecules, chemical elements, and wave mechanics are carefully explored and discussed, as are atomic radiation, light, and energy. This complicated body of information, ordinarily too overwhelming for the layman, is condensed, and its technical complexities simplified.

Part IV deals with life, the nature of living creatures down to the most minute aspects of their existence. It is concerned with reproduction and heredity, the growing process of the organism from conception to death. Here also, the focus is on man, as both an organic structure and a psychological being. The complex functions of the brain and man's thought processes, instincts and reflexes come under discussion, as do his intellect and his conscious and unconscious patterns of behavior. Life is examined in the smallest microbe, in the most fragile flower, in the most exotic insect, in the complex chromosome of a human being.

Although this book is directed mainly to the student reader, its contents and approach make it, we are confident, an effective guide for anyone who seeks a general understanding of modern scientific thought and achievement.

We wish to thank the many individuals, organizations, and institutions who have contributed information, guidance, and visual material. Above all, this undertaking would not have been possible without our editor and adapter, Norman Rudnick, whose expert advice, technical experience, and perceptive writing have made this publication, we feel, a notable achievement in the popularization of science.

THE PUBLISHERS

Contents

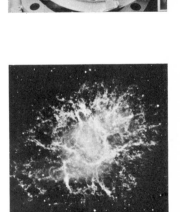

Introduction

MAN IN HIS UNIVERSE is like a baby in a strange room. Just as a baby reaches out to finger or taste all the mysterious objects in the room, so man's curiosity is excited by the wonderful sights, sounds, and smells that greet him whichever way he turns. Above him are the vastness of the starry skies, the blaze of the sun, the cool silver of the moon. Around him are the wonders of his earthly home, from the grandeur of a mountain landscape to the microscopic scurryings in a grain of dust or a droplet of water. Most wonderful of all, there is the human body itself.

Man looks, touches, sniffs, licks, and listens. Above all, he thinks. Each mystery he solves about how things are and what makes them that way does more than answer a question. It gives him the ability to glimpse new mysteries and ask new questions. As long as there is delight in discovery and an urge to understand, there will be no end to the strange rooms waiting to be entered.

Consider the things you see around you. You are aware of your own body, your room, your house. Through the window you see the street, the familiar objects of your neighborhood, a candy store, a fire hydrant, a lamppost, a ball flying through the air to bounce in smaller and smaller arcs until it comes to rest against the curb. Above the trees the sky is sunny with a sliver of moon still visible. The ball is red, the sky is blue, but the windshield of the car parked at the corner has no color and you can see through it. There is water stirring restlessly in the pond, and the stone a boy sends skipping over the surface eventually sinks with a plunk at the very spot you skated on last winter.

You see nothing between you and the tree and a gust of nothing rustles the leaves. By swishing your hand about you can feel the unseen air as it cools your fingers. Equally unseen, the faint aroma of frying bacon floats in your window, set adrift from some distant kitchen.

It is a world of sensation and there is pleasure just in the sensing of it. But there is a deeper satisfaction in looking beyond these sensations to wonder if everything is just happening or if there is a hidden connection between the transparent air and the transparent window, the bouncing ball and the rustling leaves, the sun and the stone.

Science is the search for these hidden connections.

These connections are sometimes hard to find. It took man thousands of years to discover that the earth moves around the sun and not the sun around the earth. The scientist is the expert who makes sense out of this kind of confusing evidence, while others fail because they lack the necessary training, skills, or perseverance. The scientist breaks the evidence down into its simplest parts, then puts it together again according to a pattern he thinks it follows. For example, he may study the bright spots in the dark sky, note how they seem to move, then make a guess at what they are and what path they are traveling. He will test his guess by further observations and by checking with the studies of other scientists to see if the bright spots behave as predicted. If his guess seems to be right, he will think of it as a hypothesis, and will then develop a theory to explain what is happening. After the theory has passed all its examinations by other scientists and further observations, it may graduate from a theory to a law. Some theories have become successful laws, like Newton's Law of Universal Gravitation, but others have remained only hopeful guesses. Some laws, apparently proven beyond reasonable doubt, have crumbled before new discoveries that disagreed with them; and some, like the laws of conservation of mass and energy, seem less complete than before. Later, we will deal with these laws again. When a law fails in science, no Congress is needed to repeal it.

In the pages that follow we are going to make a grand tour of the world, the universe and beyond, with many stops along the way. Our guide will be the work of thousands of scientists who have been there before us as explorers and pioneers mapping the wilderness. We will survey our world of sun and planets, and peer beyond our world to other worlds dimly visible at distances so great they stretch our imagination. We will come to earth and watch the oceans and mountains form and change until there appears the familiar face of the globe we know today. We will learn how man laboriously and painstakingly uncovered the elements of which the earth is made and then broke these down into smaller and smaller bits of matter until he thought he had reached the smallest there could ever be. Then we will find that he was mistaken—for within that apparently smallest bit there is almost a second "universe," so tiny and so strange it can be described only by a new, mathematical language. We will see that, in spite of this tininess and strangeness, the particles in this universe have a great importance in nuclear energy that may one day replace coal and oil. Unfortunately, they also make possible atomic and hydrogen bombs.

Lastly, we will consider living things—man, animals, plants, how they probably originated, how they reached their present state, how they reproduce themselves, and some of their interesting characteristics.

Remember that a scientific explanation is only the best that can be made at any given time. It must always change when new information requires that it do so, or when a better idea is offered.

THE UNIVERSE

THE NIGHT SKY looks like a giant fistful of glittering diamonds flung carelessly upon a black carpet. At dawn the moon and the stars fade, and the great orange disk of the sun dominates the heavens. For the several hundreds of thousands of years that creatures resembling men have lived upon the earth they have undoubtedly marveled at this spectacle. But only for the last 3000 years have astronomers seriously studied the heavens to try to find out what the sun and the moon and the gleaming fragments of stars might be.

At first they had only crude sticks along which they sighted, like aiming a rifle, noting the directions to various recognizable stars and how the directions changed with the time of the year. Instruments to measure angles and fix positions were refined. In spite of the limitations of the naked eye, a remarkable amount of information was gathered. Then came the invention of the telescope to sharpen and extend the astronomers' vision and the development of new mathematics to help interpret what they saw. During the last fifty years, scientific progress has been so rapid that we can now not only describe how the stars move but can speculate about what they are made of, how they were born, how they may die, and what makes some of them so hot.

Is the arrangement of the stars in the sky as careless as it looks? Let us look first at our closest neighbors in a neighborhood where next door means a few million miles away.

1. **The Constellation Orion and surrounding region.**

The Planetary System

WE FIND that the earth is but one of the members of a family of large, ball-shaped bodies, all circling about the parent, the sun. These are the *planets*. Each follows its own almost circular path, called an *orbit,* each at a different distance from the sun, so that some travel along much larger orbits than others. There are nine such large planets, following their individual flight plans like airplanes stacked at different elevations in the crowded air over a large city airport—except that planetary space is not crowded and the planets will never land on the sun for reasons that will become clear later in our story.

Are there only nine planets? Not really. The nine are the large ones, the obvious ones. Many smaller planets have been observed, but are not dignified by the name planet. Instead they are called *planetoids* or *asteroids,* and some 1500 of them have been found. In addition, there are those occasional visitors, the *comets,* which travel in long, stretched-out orbits like thin cigars. They appear nearby only for short periods and then disappear into space toward the faraway reaches of their orbits.

The last of the members of the planetary family are the *satellites*. A satellite is a smaller body which revolves about a particular planet, much the same as the planet itself revolves about the sun. As the planet pursues its course about the sun, the satellite is drawn along, circling the planet and hugging close, now in front, now behind, now to one side, like a frisky dog at the end of a leash romping about the heels of its master. The earth has only one satellite— the moon—but some other planets have more, and it is considered possible that some planets have satellites which have not not yet been discovered.

We have said that the planets revolve about the sun and the satellites revolve about the planets. But there is still more. As the planets move about the sun, they spin like tops or figure skaters on ice. In this way the satellites also have their movements in their orbits about their planets, some of them spinning and some not. Even

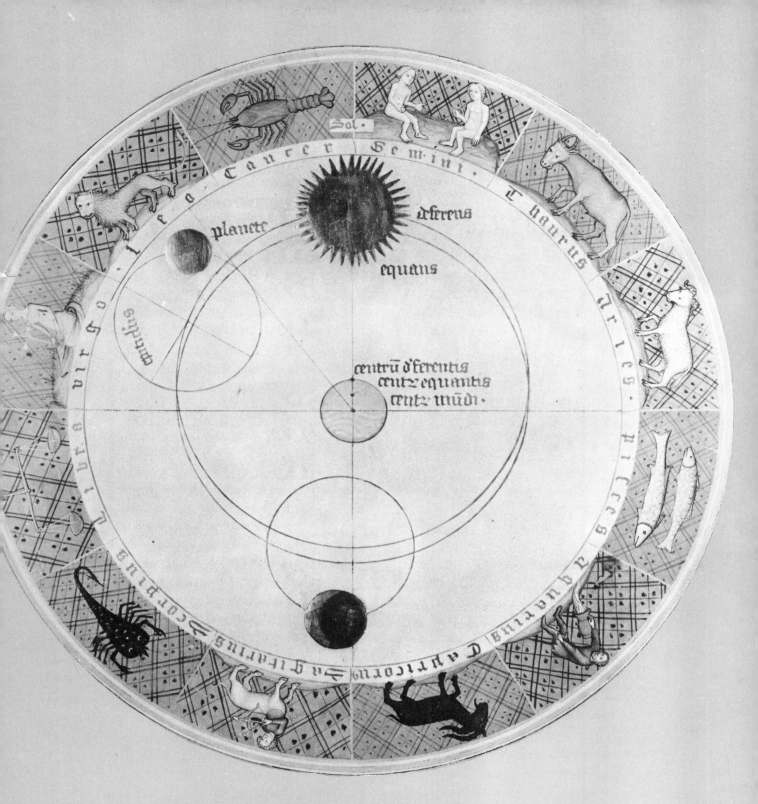

2. Greek view of the universe. *To superstitious Greeks 2000 years ago only a perfect circle was God-like enough to describe heavenly motion. The center of their universe was a round earth about which sun, moon, and planets revolved. To explain* *apparently non-circular orbits, the Greeks suggested that the heavenly bodies moved in smaller circles called epicycles while the centers of the epicycles swung around the earth in wider circles called deferents.*

15

the sun, itself, is not a fixed, stationary body; it also rotates about some larger axis, outside of our solar system, and it also seems to twist—if not spin—within itself.

These motions compounded upon motions are exactly the complications which make calculations so difficult and which baffled earlier astronomers.

Now let us talk about the members of the planetary system separately and in more detail.

THE SUN

The Size of the Sun The most important member of the planetary family is the sun. It is also the largest. To picture how large it is, compare it with the earth. The diameter of the earth is approximately 8000 miles. A trip completely around the waistline of the earth along the Equator would cover almost 25,000 miles. The diameter of the sun is over 865,000 miles, more than 100 times the size of the earth's. A belt for the sun's waistline would be 2,700,-000 miles around. If you imagine the sun as a large beach ball, about twice the size of a basketball, then the earth would be a little green pea. You can see this comparison in figure 3.

The Density of the Sun The sun, however, is not as tightly packed—as dense—as is the earth. *Density* is a measure of how much material is contained in a given space. When we say that the density of water is 62.4 pounds per cubic foot, we mean that a square box, one foot wide

by one foot long by one foot deep, completely filled with water would contain 62.4 pounds of water. Fifty-three pounds of butter, 15 pounds of cork, 490 pounds of iron, 687 pounds of lead, or 1334 pounds of platinum would fill that same box. These numbers are the densities of these substances. It is the densities of objects that determine whether they float or sink in water. Butter and cork would float because their densities are less than that of water. Iron, lead, and platinum are denser than water and would be more suitable for heavy diving boots than for floating life preservers.

We know that the sun and the earth do not have the same, uniform density everywhere on or within their huge bulks. After all, part of the earth is water and part is solids containing iron. But we can speak of average densities. These are calculated by dividing the total masses, expressed in pounds, by the volumes, expressed in cubic feet. The average density of the sun is found to be only 88.5 pounds per cubic foot, 1.42 times that of water. The average density of the earth is 344 pounds per cubic foot, 5.52 times that of water. Obviously the earth is composed more of heavy substances like iron, or cobalt, or nickel, than of materials like butter or cork.

The Temperature of the Sun The temperature of the earth can be measured with a special kind of thermometer or any of a number of other instruments designed for such purposes. However, the sun is 93,-

000,000 miles away and we do not have such long thermometers. Therefore, we have developed instruments to interpret the colors of the sun—or rather its light waves—so that we may estimate the temperature of the sun's surface.

Light is used to bring us this information. Although much more will be said about light in a later chapter, it is appropriate to explain briefly how light and color can help determine temperature.

We have all seen how the filament inside an unlit electric light bulb is a dark wire, and when the switch is turned on, the filament becomes a bright, glowing blur. Heat has made the difference, and this is a fact easily proven merely by touching the glass. Similarly, the coils in an electric toaster heat up to a reddish brightness. When molten metal is poured in a steel mill—and we have all seen this in the movies or on television—the hot liquid looks like a white river of fire.

When anything becomes hot enough, it gives off light, and the color of the light is related to the temperature. If we took color moving pictures of the wire inside a common light bulb as its temperature went up, and then showed them in slow motion, we would see the wire become first a dim

3. Size of the sun. *The sun has a diameter of 865,000 miles, about 109 times that of the earth. In volume the sun is over a million times larger than the earth and has more than 330,000 times as much mass. Despite these great dimensions, the sun is merely an average star in our Galaxy.*

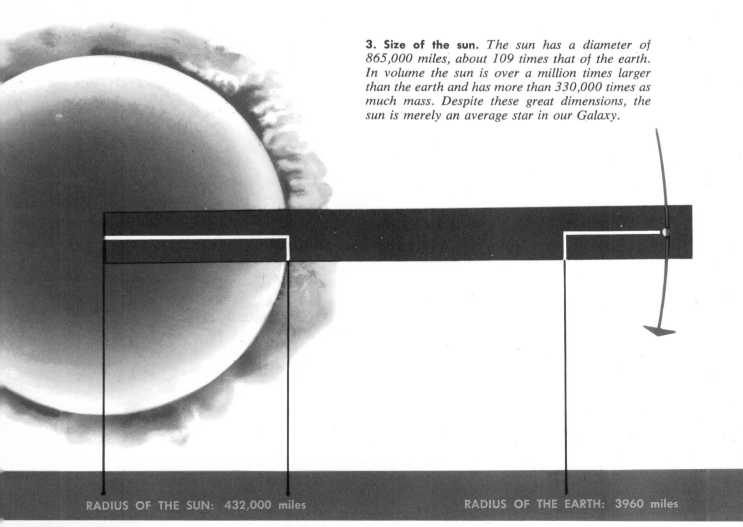

RADIUS OF THE SUN: 432,000 miles

RADIUS OF THE EARTH: 3960 miles

4. Midnight sun—Greenland. *During the northern summer, the North Pole is tilted toward the sun. From polar regions like Greenland the sun is then visible 24 hours a day, clouds permitting. The turning of the earth on its axis causes the sun to rise and dip in the sky but not set. Positions of the sun were photographed at 20-minute intervals.*

red, then a dark wine color, then bright cherry red, orange, yellow, and finally brilliant white. We can use this appearance as a rough measure of temperature as follows:

COLOR	TEMPERATURE (Degrees Fahrenheit)
Dim red	900–1000
Dark red	1200–1400
Bright red	1550–1750
Yellowish-red (orange)	1900–2100
Yellowish-white	2300–2500
White	2600–2800

Fahrenheit is the temperature scale which the weatherman uses when he forecasts that it will be 90 degrees (90° F) in the city and 80 degrees (80° F) at the beach. This is also the scale your doctor uses to check your body temperature which should be 98.6° F. Water freezes at 32° F and boils at 212° F.

But this way of measuring temperature by color does not really satisfy the scientist. People see or describe colors differently. Even if two observers can agree on the color, this locates the temperature only within very broad limits. The scientist demands more accuracy and also needs the means to measure much higher temperatures.

Besides, these colors are not pure, but are really mixtures of many colors. For example, a rainbow is the white light from the sun with all the colors separated from each other. Scientists have found that among the many colors mixed together in the light emitted by a hot object, there is always one color which is brighter than all the rest. More than this, at each temperature a different color stands out. Therefore, if we can determine which color has the greatest intensity, we will be able to know the temperature.

To do this we use an instrument called the *spectroscope*. The spectroscope can break up any light into its differently colored parts and permit us to compare the parts and decide which is the brightest. A scientist can heat objects to known temperatures and look at them through a spectroscope. He can then single out the color with the greatest brightness and match this color against the temperature that produced it. In this way he can make up a list of temperatures and, next to each, write the color which would be brightest at that temperature.

A scientist is not limited in his description of color to words like red, orange, and green. He has a method for naming colors by exact numbers in the same way that radio frequencies are numbered to distinguish one broadcasting station from another. Because the colors can be named by exact numbers, the temperatures with which they are connected can be determined accurately. More wonderful still, we can calculate the colors expected for temperatures too high to be created easily on earth.

In this way it has been found that the temperature of the surface of the sun is approximately 11,000° F. This is surely a stupendous furnace.

But if the outside of the furnace wall is so incredibly hot, what of the interior? We know the temperature of the surface of the sun because we receive light from it, but the light from the inside is blocked from our view. This forced the scientists to attack the problem indirectly. It required all the mental resources of the astronomers, the mathematicians, the physicists, the chemists, and others to invent theories as to what might be happening in the center of the sun and other hot stars to produce so much heat. The consequences of these theories were then tested by scanning the skies and by patiently carrying out experiments in laboratories. There were promising experiments which turned into frustrating failures. But the work was not wasted. The failures meant only that the theories were not perfect. However, information was gathered from experimentation, and understanding developed from thinking mathematically about the problem. This prepared the way for a few strokes of genius which caused all this labor to bear fruit. Theories developed and tested during the last fifty years have penetrated some of the most mysterious processes of nature. When these theories were applied to explain the strange results of experiments here on earth and the behavior of hot stars in space, they were magnificently confirmed. The cooperation among the various specialized branches of science that produced this sudden advance in human knowledge is now accepted as common practice.

The conclusion reached is that the temperature inside the sun is probably of the order of 35,000,000° F (figure 5) and may very well be even hotter in some places. This is not a temperature that is easy to visualize but it is something to think about when you feel you are sweltering on a 90° F day in July.

5. Temperature of the sun. *The sun's immense quantity of heat comes mainly from the conversion of hydrogen into helium. These nuclear reactions produce temperatures ranging from millions of degrees at the center to thousands at the surface. Gases in the surrounding atmosphere are even hotter than the surface, ranging up to about 2 million degrees in temperature.*

The Source of the Sun's Heat   This enormous incandescent globe, more than 865,000 miles across, with a surface temperature of 11,000° F and an inner temperature of 35,000,000° F, is continually sending out vast quantities of energy in all directions. Each second the sun radiates the same amount of heat that would be produced by completely burning 10 million billion tons of coal. This happens every second and has been going on between 5 and 10 billion years.

As the heat spreads out from the sun, the farther away it reaches, the more thinly divided it becomes. By the time it has traveled outward far enough to touch the earth, it is like a fine spray. The portion

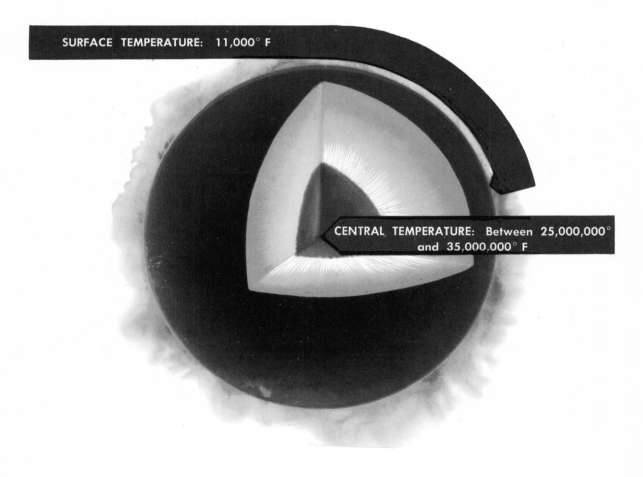

SURFACE TEMPERATURE: 11,000° F

CENTRAL TEMPERATURE: Between 25,000,000° and 35,000,000° F

of the sun's heat that falls on the surface of the earth is therefore like the few droplets of water that fall on a pebble in a light summer rain. In numbers, the heat received by the earth is only one-half of a billionth of the total heat radiated by the sun. This is like fifty cents out of a billion dollars.

Yet this fifty cents' worth is what keeps us alive. This is the heat which melts ice, causes rivers to flow, oceans to evaporate, clouds to form, winds to blow, and rain to fall. It grows trees, opens blossoms, and ripens fruit. The food that feeds us, the coal and oil that warm us and run our factories and automobiles, almost every element of our daily existence can be traced back to that little splatter of the sun's heat on the surface of the earth.

No wonder that many ancient peoples centered their religions about the sun. The Incas, who lived in Peru in South America at the time of Columbus, went up on mountainous terraces to greet the rising sun, worshipping it as the god of day and the king of light. Although they certainly knew nothing of the true magnitude of the sun and its fierce temperature, they sensed their dependence on its heat and revered the sun as their father and protector.

But where does all this energy that the sun spends so extravagantly come from? We mentioned before how much coal would have to be burned each second to stoke the sun's furnace. But geologists, who have ways to estimate the age of the sun, say that the sun has been performing like this for at least 5 billion years. This is a good many seconds. Is it possible that there could be on the sun some fuel like coal or oil in such quantities that 10 million billion tons of it could be burned every second for 5 billion years? Well, if the entire sun were one huge lump of coal burning at such a rate, there would be only ashes left in about 6000 years.

What then is the source of the sun's heat? Only since Albert Einstein conceived the *theory of relativity* at the beginning of this century has a likely answer to this question been found.

Before Einstein there were two separate scientific laws which were considered to be obeyed perfectly by everything in the universe. One was the *law of conservation of matter*. This stated that the amount of material you had left after any kind of process or chemical reaction must be the same as the amount you started with. The material might change form, as when a liquid like water evaporates to become a gas, but the total weight before and after must be identical.

The second was the *law of conservation of energy*. This said that the amount of energy you end with must be exactly the same as the amount of energy you had at the beginning. Energy can be neither created nor destroyed; it can only be transformed. When electricity flows in the heating element in an electric stove, electrical energy is converted into heat energy. The form changes, but none is lost. The amount of heat produced is equal to the amount of electrical energy consumed.

What Einstein found was that the tidy

distinction between matter and energy does not exist. Matter, and the weight that goes with it, is forever disappearing and energy appearing in its place. Also, energy disappears and matter is found in its place. The reason this was discovered only recently is that it usually happens on a very small scale. Now we have radioactive materials like radium and new, small particles with strange names like mesons, positrons, and neutrinos, in which relatively large amounts of matter become energy. Some of these new particles are found only in cosmic rays that come to us from outer space, or are created in machines like the cyclotron.

Now that we know how to look, we find that matter and energy have been interchangeable all along. For example, when coal burns, the carbon in coal combines with the oxygen in air to form a new substance called carbon dioxide. Carbon dioxide is a gas and goes up the chimney with the smoke. If we catch the carbon dioxide and weigh it, we find its weight is the same as the combined weights of the carbon and oxygen that went into its making. This apparently proves the law of conservation of matter. Einstein has shown us that some matter must be lost to produce the heat and light energy given off during burning. His theory tells us how to figure the quantity of matter that is lost. It turns out that this is so small, it is no wonder our most sensitive scales and balances cannot detect it.

Since the law of conservation of matter holds so well, if not perfectly, in all chemical reactions, very little matter is changed into energy. This applies even to great dynamite explosions. Compared to the heat of the sun, the heat of the biggest chemical explosion is like a tiny spark in a forest fire. The sun's heat must be produced by a completely different process. Hans Bethe, a modern physicist, described such a process. If four bits or atoms of hydrogen combine in a complex way, the end result is one bit of helium. The one helium has much less mass than the four hydrogens so an enormous amount of energy is released. Something like this happens in the most violent man-made explosion on earth, the detonation of a hydrogen bomb.

The making of helium from hydrogen is not like the making of carbon dioxide from carbon and oxygen. In carbon dioxide the carbon and oxygen are tied together, but they retain some identity as carbon and oxygen. This is a *chemical reaction*. In helium the original hydrogens are no longer present in any recognizable form. It is like changing silver into gold. This is a *nuclear reaction*. To start the chemical reaction, the coal must first be made hot enough in the presence of oxygen. We call this "lighting the fire." To light the nuclear fire requires a starting

6. Spectra from various sources. *The number of lines in a spectrum is related to the number of values of energy (energy levels) available to the emitting atoms. Since the levels are different for each type of atom, an atom can be identified by its spectrum as a man is by his fingerprints. When the atom is linked to other atoms, as in a gas molecule or the crystals of a solid, the energy levels may be so numerous the spectral lines broaden into bands or into a continuous spectrum.*

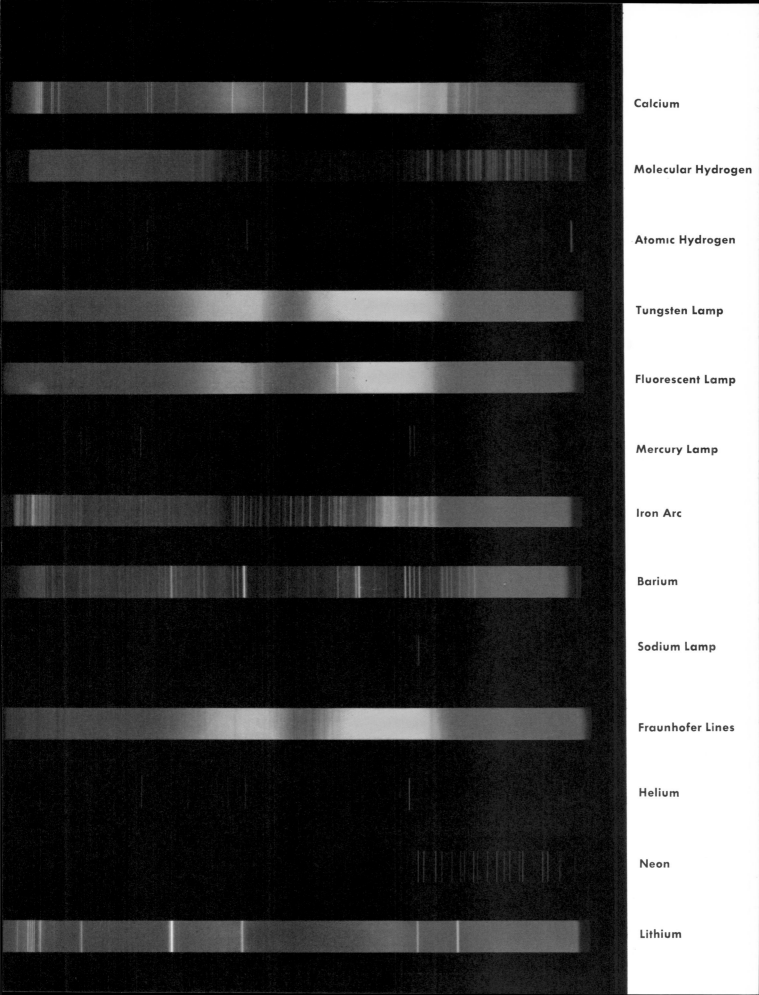

Calcium

Molecular Hydrogen

Atomic Hydrogen

Tungsten Lamp

Fluorescent Lamp

Mercury Lamp

Iron Arc

Barium

Sodium Lamp

Fraunhofer Lines

Helium

Neon

Lithium

temperature that may be as high as millions of degrees. This is why it occurs only at the center of the sun and other hot stars.

If instead of *burning* coal, we could convert it completely into energy by some nuclear process, one pound would supply the needs of all the homes, factories, electric powerhouses, railroads, and steamships of a country the size of Italy for one month. The biggest transatlantic ocean liner could make a round trip to Europe on a cinder.

Because small amounts of matter contain so much energy, it is understandable that the sun has remained so hot for so long. In fact, the supply of hydrogen is great enough that the sun is in no danger of growing dim for well over 10 or 20 billion years.

What the Sun Is Made Of Before considering what the sun is made of, it might be well to take a closer look at the earth.

Making a list of the different substances we find on earth is a little like taking a census of the human population. We could cover miles of paper with names. When we thought we were finished, we would discover that some people had not been home when we called, we had forgotten some miners down in the earth, a few eccentrics had hidden from us in their attics, and millions of babies were born while we were writing.

Something similar happens when we take a census of the different materials on earth. We can write long lists of solids like gold, iron, nickel, lead, wood, sand, rock, wax, salt, and plastic. Then there are liquids like oil, water, mercury, and blood; or gases like oxygen, neon, helium, carbon dioxide, and steam. While we write, however, new substances are being discovered, created in laboratories, or being dug from the earth. New combinations of old materials are forever being born in steel mills and plastics factories. Is it hopeless to try to describe everything on earth and keep up with the newcomers? No, because all of these different materials are not as unrelated to each other as you might think.

There are only twenty-six letters in the alphabet, yet there is no end to the number of words that can be made from them. In a sense, these twenty-six letters describe every word in English and in many foreign languages. This includes not only present-day words, but also old words we no longer use and new words that have not yet been invented.

It has been found that everything on earth—solid, liquid, or gas—is made up of a group of simple *elements* which are like letters in a chemical alphabet. These elements are joined together in different ways to form substances the way letters are joined to form words. Some substances are very simple. They are the elements themselves, like words composed of only one letter. Some of these elements are nickel, iron, copper, aluminum, and sulfur, which are like the one-letter words "I" and "a." Carbon monoxide, the deadly gas that collects in a garage when the car motor is left running, is like the word "of."

24

It is made of one carbon and one oxygen. Carbon dioxide, which we met before, is like the word "off," because there are one carbon and two oxygens. Other substances have many elements in them, the most complicated of all being living things like animals and plants.

It is now known that there are at least 103 elements that make up the things we find on earth. The names of these elements range from actinium to zirconium. If, in our imagination, we could grind an element like carbon into an ever finer and finer powder, and then continue to divide the powder grains into still smaller parts, we would eventually arrive at a tiny, invisible particle which could not be made smaller and still be a particle of carbon. This smallest particle of a simple element is called an *atom*. Some elements like oxygen cannot exist freely as single atoms but gather into clusters of two atoms. The atom is, therefore, the smallest particle of an element but not necessarily the smallest amount of the element which can exist freely in nature. This difference will be considered later under the subject of molecules.

We now know that the atom of an element is not the simplest form of matter. It is itself composed of mysterious, smaller particles bound tightly together. Scientists have learned to break atoms apart and put the parts together again, sometimes rearranging them. In fact, by adding parts of broken atoms to existing elements scientists have succeeded in creating new elements never encountered before. Only 92 of the elements can normally be found occurring naturally. The others, like the man-made elements berkelium and americium, have heavy, unstable atoms which live for only a short time after they are born. When they die, they become one of the more stable 92 elements. Radioactivity is the process by which certain atoms change spontaneously into other atoms. Some of the 92 have also been found to be radioactive, but they decay much more slowly. Since they live longer, they are more abundant in the world around us.

Are the sun and the planets and the distant stars made of the same elements we find on earth? Or does each heavenly body have its own special list? Luckily, it turns out that the one list is all we need.

To find out what the sun is composed of, we turn again to the spectroscope. We learned before that the light from a hot, luminous object is seen through the spectroscope as a number of different colors. The rainbow is the spectroscopic pattern produced by light from the hot surface of the sun. This rainbow type of pattern is called a *continuous spectrum,* because we cannot tell where one color ends and the next begins. A broad band of red changes gradually into orange; the orange fades gently into yellow. This is repeated through green, blue, and violet.

If we sight the spectroscope on a glowing gas instead of a hot, solid body, we see a different image. Instead of smears of color that blend into each other, we find a series of thin, sharp lines of color against a dark background. Each line has the

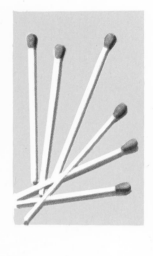

7. Familiar forms of matter. *Most matter is composed of various arrangements of about 90 chemical elements. With some rare and man-made elements, the total number is now at least 103 and may rise. We find sulfur in match heads, iron in steel keys, nickel in some coins, and silver in many rings. The sun, indeed all bodies in the universe, is made of the same elements found on earth.*

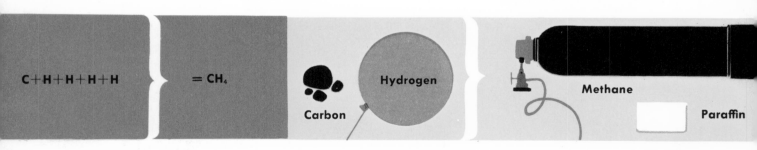

C + H + H + H + H = CH₄ Carbon Hydrogen Methane Paraffin

8. Elements, compounds and mixtures. *Atoms of elements combine to form compounds somewhat the way letters combine to form words. When one atom of carbon (abundant in bits of charcoal) combines with four atoms of hydrogen (found in the lighter-than-air gas that makes balloons rise), the result is a molecule of the compound methane, an inflammable gas. Paraffin wax is a mixture of methane-like compounds that are intimately blended but have not reacted chemically with each other.*

9. Types of spectra. *The colors found in most light can be separated into a spectrum with the use of a spectroscope. (A) A hot solid glows with all the colors and gives a continuous spectrum. (B) A luminous gas of single atoms emits only certain definite colors, which appear as a bright line spectrum. (C) A cool gas absorbs colors from light passing through it, leaving a dark line spectrum. (D) Sunlight yields both continuous and line spectra.*

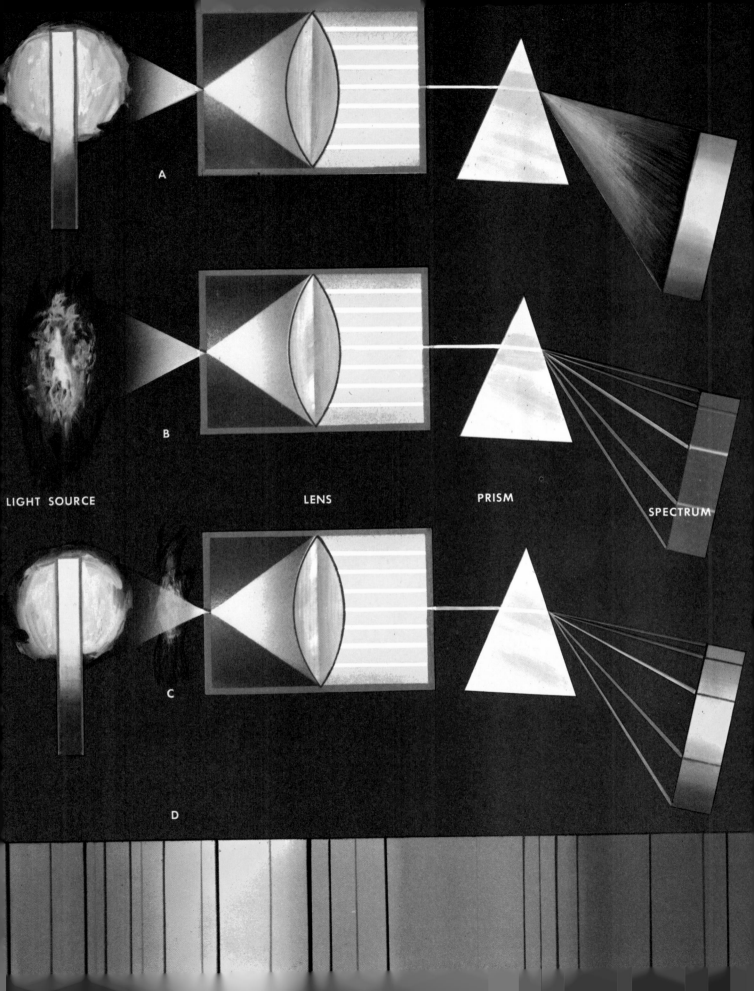

LIGHT SOURCE   LENS   PRISM   SPECTRUM

A

B

C

D

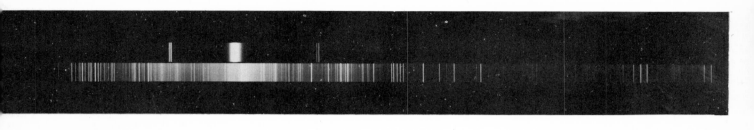

10. Spectra of sodium and iron. *Bright line spectra emitted by the excited atoms of chemical elements may contain few or many lines. Iron has many more lines than sodium. Visible lines appear as pure colors. However, photographic film sensitive to invisible infrared and ultraviolet light will record more lines than the eye can detect.*

11. Spectrum of light from the sun. *Exceptionally wide separation of the colors in sunlight is made with a special instrument called a spectrohelio-graph, an adaptation of the spectroscope. The continuous color spectrum is cut into two lengths, stretching from violet (upper left edge) to red (lower right edge). Dark lines are missing colors absorbed by gases in sun's atmosphere. Numbers are wave lengths.*

same color that formerly existed at that same spot in the spectroscope picture when a rainbow was seen. It is as if we cut thin, vertical slits here and there in a strip of black paper and then laid the strip over the rainbow. The rainbow is blacked out, and color shows through only where there are slits. The colored lines may be few or many, closely spaced in clusters or widely spaced with dark gaps in between. Such a pattern is called a *bright line spectrum*. The glowing gas may be given off by a hot body when it is vaporized in a hot electric arc. Or it may be a relatively cool gas through which electricity is passed, as in a neon sign.

However it is done, when an element of matter is excited in the form of a glow-

ing gas, it displays its own line spectrum in the spectroscope. This is different from the bright line spectrum of every other element. It is the element's fingerprint. Some elements like sodium or hydrogen have very few lines. Some like iron have almost too many to count. Since the color of a line depends on where it happens to fall in the spectroscope picture, we can describe the line by its position as well as by its color. This is done by measuring how far the line is from some convenient reference point. The number of lines and their positions in the bright line spectrum completely identify an element. It is usually enough to find only a few of the most prominent lines of a given element to be sure that element is present in the gas we are studying. We do not have to locate every line.

If we are looking at an unknown mixture of gases that exhibits lines in a spectroscope, we will see all the lines of all the elements in the mixture. By matching the lines we see with the known lines of the

elements, we can pick out the elements actually present.

Now let us point our spectroscope at the sun again. We see the rainbow. Now that we know about bright line spectrums, we look more sharply for lines. We find them —many of them—but we also see a surprising thing. The lines are mostly black ones set against the rainbow background, instead of the brightly colored lines we were led to expect.

This riddle was studied by Fraunhofer early in the nineteenth century, and the black lines were named after him. It was found that the lines occurred exactly where the lines of many known elements should fall. Their lack of color is due to *absorption*. Through a red glass the sun looks red. This is because the red glass absorbs all the other colors in the sun's light and passes only the red. It was learned by experiment that gases can also absorb colors. If we look at the sun through a bottleful of gas that absorbs green, the green will be missing from the light reaching our eyes.

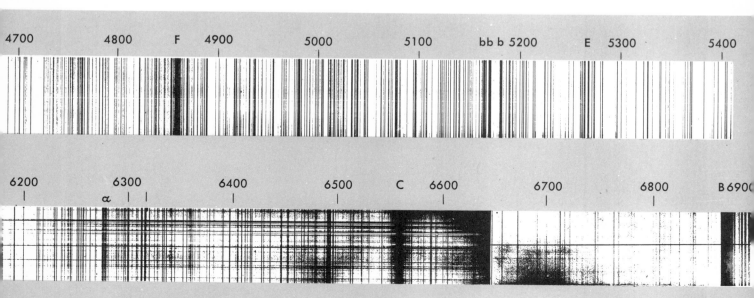

It was also found that the gases may absorb not whole bands of color, but only parts of the color spectrum. In fact, a cool gas absorbs exactly those thin-line portions of the color spectrum that correspond to the bright line spectrum the gas emits when heated to glowing.

What happens on the sun is this. The hot ball of the sun is surrounded by an atmosphere of lighter, cooler gas, just as the earth is surrounded by air. The light, carrying the colors of the rainbow, is emitted by the hot surface of the sun, but must pass through the gaseous atmosphere of the sun before reaching the earth. Each element present in the sun's atmosphere steals from the rainbow, by absorption, the colors of its own line spectrum. What we see on earth through our spectroscope is the continuous rainbow spectrum but with the stolen portions missing.

Therefore, if we concentrate on the positions of these black lines and do not worry because they lack the proper colors, we can still identify the various elements that have caused them.

In this way we have determined which elements are on the sun from a distance of 93,000,000 miles. At least 47 of the basic 92 elements are found. The others may be there, but in quantities too small to be detectable. The 47 do not exist on the sun in the same proportions as on the earth. About 80 per cent of the sun is hydrogen, the nuclear fuel that furnishes the sun's heat. Another 19 per cent is helium. All the other elements present make up the remaining 1 per cent.

Strangeness of the Sun's Surface   A total eclipse of the sun was announced for July 8, 1842. On that day the moon was due to pass directly between the sun and the earth. This would darken the sun entirely except for a bright halo around the rim of the moon's shadow. The astronomers prepared their instruments with excitement, praying for clear skies. When the impatiently awaited moment came, the sun presented such a spectacular and unexpected display that the astronomers were paralyzed with wonder. They forgot their instruments completely. Before they could recover to perform their scientific tasks, the moon had drifted on, the sun was slowly reappearing, and it was too late.

What had amazed them was a number of long tongues of fire erupting from the sun like brilliant flames. Because of their astonishment, the astronomers were like witnesses at an accident. Nobody could agree with anybody else as to what had actually taken place. Some had seen two such flames, some three, some large ones, some small ones, some had seen three with jagged edges all shooting from the top of the sun at one time. The one point of agreement was that these tongues of fire really existed. These were later called *solar*

12. Corona during solar eclipse. *The body of the sun is hidden behind the moon, leaving the corona visible around the edge of the shadow. A jet aircraft at 45,000 feet chased the shadow at a speed of 18 miles per minute, permitting observation for almost seven minutes, during which this photograph was taken. The shadow moved over the earth at 27.6 miles per minute, restricting stationary ground observation to only two minutes.*

13. Surface of the sun. *In a highly magnified view, the surface of the sun appears granulated or pebbled. The granules are bubbles of hot gas that rise from the interior, mix with the surface, and then sink back again. Since they are temporarily hotter than the surrounding surface, they appear as bright cells.*

prominences and are seen in figures 15–19.

Actually, as far back as 1239, people had claimed to have seen such flares with their naked eyes. They were not taken seriously. It was claimed that their eyes had played tricks, that they had seen an optical illusion. In 1842 there could no longer be any doubt. The solar prominences were really there.

The next total eclipse of the sun was scheduled to take place in Sweden in 1851. This time an expedition was organized and carefully rehearsed in advance by the director of the Greenwich Observatory, a world-famous astronomical institution in England. Their luck held and the weather was good. Now when the sun dimmed, the astronomers were ready, the instruments were in position, and the observations made were in general agreement. Each succeeding eclipse and each improvement in instruments furnished more information until the mystery was cleared up.

The prominences are great fiery arms of incandescent hydrogen gas hurled out of the sun to enormous distances. Some reach out no less than 500,000 miles, almost as long as 65 earths strung out like a row of bowling balls.

These flares erupt suddenly and violently, sometimes becoming detached to hang free in space. Others rise straight and then bend to one side like the smoke from a chimney caught by a high wind. Other shapes resemble scenes traced by sparkling fireworks at Fourth of July celebrations. There are magnificent palm trees, gracefully curved, and strange flowers with thin,

14. Annular eclipse of the sun. *The distances between sun and earth and between moon and earth are not always the same. Under certain conditions during a solar eclipse, when the sun is especially close and the moon especially far away, the moon does not hide the entire body of the sun. An annulus, or ring, of the sun remains uncovered around the rim.*

threadlike stems that swell into a broad swirl of petals at the top. Still others stretch out like floating clouds of the solar sky.

These marvelous forms do not really hang or float but are driven by an internal violence. They burst from the sun at speeds of up to a thousand miles a second to bend and twist and break. A bullet travels only a few thousand feet a second. When there is an eruption of sun flares, most of the turbulent activity is compressed into the space of a few days.

Solar flares are not the only signs of rest-

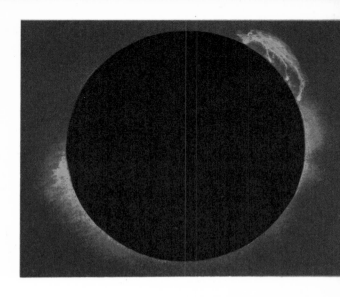

15-19. Solar prominences. *Flares of hot gases flung out from the sun create a spectacular display of incandescent shapes. The arches, loops, sprays, and columns are clues to the forces that generate and form the flares. Visible portions of the prominences may extend for over half a million miles. Outbursts are often accompanied by radio interference on earth and the emission of streams of particles that pose a hazard to space travel.*

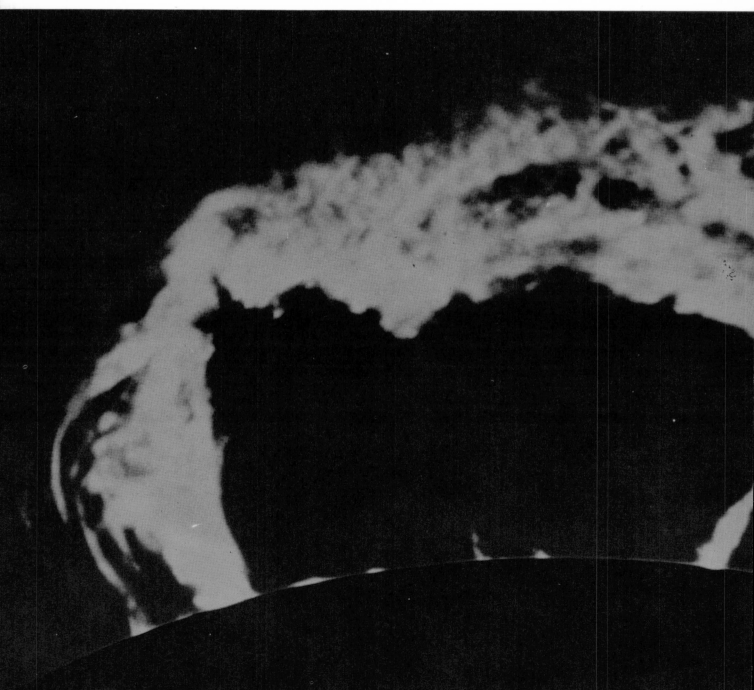

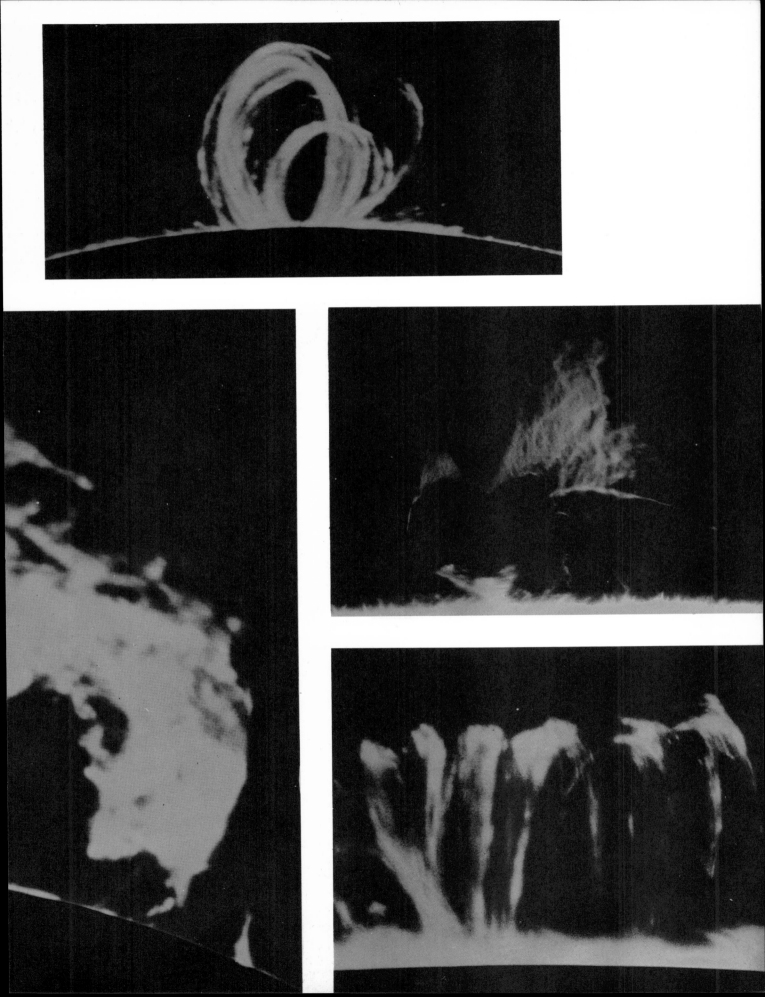

20. Sun flare at maximum brilliance. *An erupting flare creates a bright patch on the face of the sun at upper right. A flare is a solar explosion that shoots hot gas far out into space. Flares were discovered projecting out from the sun's disk during a total eclipse when the central blinding glare was dimmed by the moon's shadow. With modern equipment these bright patches can be seen against the disk itself.*

21. Northern lights. *Northern lights (aurora borealis) and southern lights (aurora australis) are striking displays occasionally seen in the night sky of polar regions. They may be a diffuse glow, streamers of red, a bright arc of color, or rippling curtains of tinted light hanging in the sky. Auroras frequently follow large solar flares. The flares emit charged particles which are channeled to the north and south poles by the earth's magnetic field.*

lessness on the sun. If you look closely at a sharp photograph of the sun's face, you see dark blemishes scattered here and there. These are called *sunspots* (figure 22). Some are small, with diameters of as little as 500 miles. The largest may be 150,000 miles across, almost twenty times the diameter of the earth. Some last for only a few days, whereas others may persist for over a hundred days.

There are regular variations in the number of sunspots. At times the face of the sun may be almost clear. Then the number of spots will gradually increase until a peak is reached. After this, the number gradually diminishes. These peaks of sunspot activity recur every eleven years, like outbreaks of solar measles.

Sunspots are actually huge whirlpools of hot gas. They are like whirling windstorms, such as tornadoes, that attack the face of the earth. Just as the temperature

at the center of a tornado is lower than in the surrounding area, so the temperature at a sunspot is cooler than the rest of the sun's surface, about 7000°F as compared with 11,000°F. This is one of the reasons the spots stand out as dark regions.

Sunspots are of interest not only to the world of astronomy. They concern all of us. A period of increased sunspot activity is usually accompanied by what are known as "magnetic storms" that occur here on earth. During these storms radio, telegraph, television, and telephone communication can be disrupted. Compass needles on ships or on Boy Scouts' belts can be affected. There is generally a flare-up of "northern lights." These are those weird, illuminated curtains of changing colors that seem to hang in the sky near the north and south poles ("southern lights"). It is even considered possible that sunspots may have some influence on our weather.

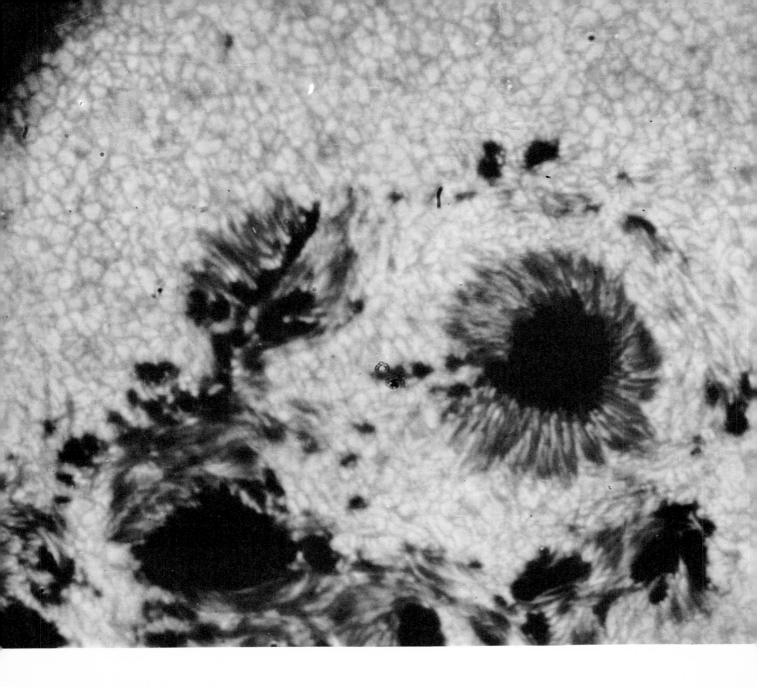

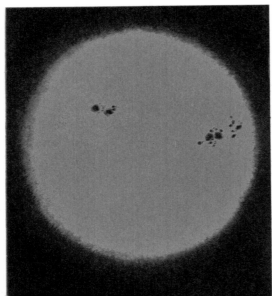

22. Sunspots. *Close-up image of an active group of sunspots was photographed from a balloon at 80,000 feet. The absence of dense atmosphere and dust produced unprecedented sharpness of the image. Granules and details of spots are clearly visible. Spots consist of a dark core of relatively cool gases embedded in a strong magnetic field.*

At left is an artist's conception of sunspots as they would appear in relation to the entire surface of the sun.

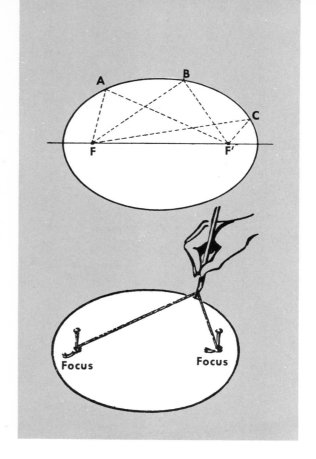

THE PLANETS

The Orbits of the Planets We said before that the planetary orbits were almost circles. They are really a special curve called an *ellipse*. In mathematics an ellipse is a curve drawn so that the sum of the distances from a point on the curve to two fixed points inside the curve is always the same. This will be clearer from the drawing in figure 23, which shows how to construct an ellipse. The two fixed points are the nails driven into a large, flat board. Each is called a *focus* of the ellipse, and the two together are called *foci*. A string is cut longer than the spacing between the nails and each end is tied to a nail. With the point of a pencil, the string is pulled tight. The string now has two legs, one joining the pencil point to one nail, or focus, the other to the other focus. These legs are the two distances mentioned in the definition. The sum of these two distances is just the length of the string. This is always the same, as the definition requires, since we assume that the string does not shrink or stretch. The pencil point is a point on the curve. If we move the pencil around, always keeping it pressed tightly against the string so that the two legs are straight, the pencil will draw an ellipse. If F and F' represent the foci, and A, B, and C are three points on the ellipse—that is, three different positions of the pencil point—then we can describe the ellipse mathematically. AF is a way of writing the distance from A to F. AF' is a way of writing the distance from A to F'. $AF + AF'$ is a way of writing

23. Construction of an ellipse. *The sum of the distances from a point on the curve (A, B, or C) to two fixed points inside the curve (F or F') will always be the same. (See text for a full description of method.)*

the addition of the two distances. This is the length of the string. Mathematically, then,

$$AF + AF' = BF + BF' = CF + CF' = \ldots$$

The three dots indicate that we could sum the pairs of distances from any point on the ellipse to the foci and the answer would be the same.

If we keep the same length of string, but move the foci closer together, the ellipse becomes more circular. In fact, if we put the two foci right on top of each other by tying both ends of the string to one nail, the moving pencil will draw a circle. A circle is merely a special kind of ellipse. If we move the foci farther apart, the ellipse becomes oval-shaped, then long and thin like a barely open slit. If we move the foci so far apart that the string just reaches from one to the other, then the pencil cannot push the string to one side at all. There is no slack in the string. The pencil now moves along the string from one focus to the other and draws a straight line. This is a completely closed ellipse. Therefore, the straight line itself can be considered a special case of an ellipse.

In the solar system the sun is at one focus of all the ellipses representing the orbits of the planets. The other focus is slightly different for each planet. It is never very far from the sun. Therefore, we have the case where the two foci are close together and the elliptical orbits are wide and round, almost like circles.

The orbits of the comets are examples of ellipses where the two foci are far apart. These ellipses are narrow and elongated.

In the case of many satellites, the orbits are also ellipses. The parent planet in each case occupies one of the foci.

Gravitation   What is it that keeps these huge balls whirling in space like a magic juggling act? Why do they travel in elliptical orbits? The answer was discovered by Sir Isaac Newton, a great genius who contributed to almost every branch of science in the seventeenth century. More will be said about Newton's achievements in a later chapter.

Newton showed that the heavenly bodies must attract each other. Although the force they exert on each other is like the pull of a magnet on a steel pin, it is not magnetism. It is called *gravitation*. The strength of the force between bodies is greater if the bodies are large and dense and if they are close together. It is weaker if the bodies are smaller and lighter and if they are farther apart. The sun is the most massive of the members of the planetary system. Therefore, the force of attraction between the sun and each of the planets is much greater than the force between any two planets themselves. The distance between a planet and its satellite is relatively small, however, so that the force of attraction between planet and satellite is greater than between satellite and sun. The satellite obeys the pull of the planet rather than that of the sun.

It was demonstrated mathematically by Newton that a gravitational attraction between the sun and each planet would cause the planet to move along an elliptical path. Although the attraction between planets is very small compared with the attraction to the sun, the interplanetary attraction does exist. It exerts enough of a pull on each planet to change the shape of the orbits very slightly. This slight effect was calculated and found to be large enough so that it could be observed.

This effect had important consequences. About 1840 it was decided that the planet Uranus was seriously misbehaving. It was straying from the path calculated from Newton's discoveries. A bold suggestion was made that there might be some unseen heavenly body pulling Uranus off course.

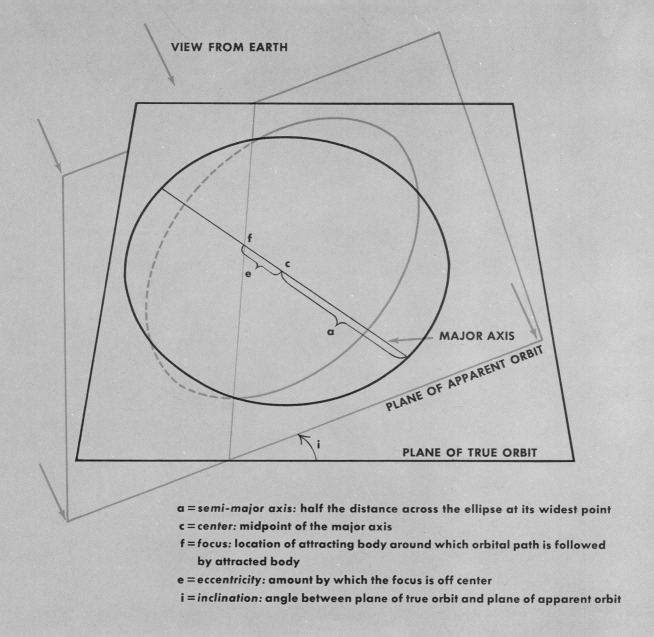

VIEW FROM EARTH

f

e c

a

MAJOR AXIS

PLANE OF APPARENT ORBIT

i

PLANE OF TRUE ORBIT

a = *semi-major axis*: half the distance across the ellipse at its widest point

c = *center*: midpoint of the major axis

f = *focus*: location of attracting body around which orbital path is followed by attracted body

e = *eccentricity*: amount by which the focus is off center

i = *inclination*: angle between plane of true orbit and plane of apparent orbit

24. Elements of an elliptic orbit. *An orbit is described by its focus, semi-major axis, semi-minor axis (half the width at the narrowest point), and the distance from center to focus (eccentricity). A large eccentricity signifies a long, narrow ellipse. From earth, the orbit seems to lie in a plane perpendicular to the line of view, usually tilted at some angle (i) to the plane in which the orbit truly lies.*

The discovery of the planet Neptune followed in a brilliant confirmation of Newton's theories.

If the sun exerts such a powerful pull on the planets, why don't they fall into the fiery furnace? After all, if a stone is released, the attraction between it and the earth immediately causes it to fall to the ground. Why doesn't the moon fall to the earth like the stone?

The answer is illustrated in figure 25. The curved, heavy black band represents the surface of the earth. In panel I, if a stone is simply dropped from a height at point *A*, it falls straight to the earth with a thud at point *B*. If instead of just dropping it, we toss it away from us horizontally from point *A*, it will land some distance away at point *C*. If we throw it harder and harder, it will land progressively farther away at point *D*, then point *E*, until, if we could throw it hard enough, it would not land on the earth at all. Where would it go?

To answer this question, let us imagine that there is no air resistance to slow the stone down. When we throw the stone in a horizontal direction, it begins its flight along a straight line represented by the dark arrow in panel II. Immediately the

gravitational pull on the stone causes the path to curve down toward the earth. The motion is now a combination of two motions, one parallel to the earth's surface deriving from the initial throw, and the second a falling toward the earth induced by the earth's attraction. Without air resistance, the motion parallel to the earth's surface is not diminished. Therefore, if the stone is thrown hard enough to barely miss the earth as the earth's attraction pulls it down, the stone will continue to circle the earth without ever hitting it. Compared with the downward pull of the earth, the forward speed of the stone will always be

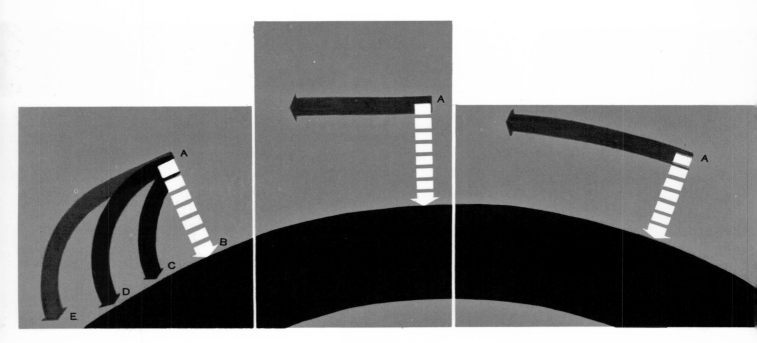

25. Why the moon does not fall to earth. *An object dropped from a height falls straight to earth. If thrown horizontally when released, it lands some distance away. If given enough horizontal speed, it will clear the edge of the earth as it falls. The moon is really falling, but, speeding sideways as it falls, it overshoots and always misses the earth. A man-made satellite encounters air resistance which slows down the sideways motion, and eventually the satellite spirals into the earth.*

26. Relative size of the sun and planets. *Compared to the sun the nine planets appear quite small. The diameter of the sun is almost 10 times that of Jupiter, the largest planet in our solar system.*

MERCURY   VENUS   EARTH   MARS   JUPITER   SATURN   URANUS   NEPTUNE   PLUTO

27. Asteroids. *Between Mars and Jupiter there are a large number of small planets called planetoids or asteroids. They range in size from a few miles to almost 500 miles in diameter. More than 6000 asteroids have been observed to date.*

28. Space trail of the earth. *As the earth travels in a wide swing about the sun, it leaves a wake of very thin gas. Air molecules of the upper atmosphere, only weakly attracted by gravity because of their great distance from the earth, escape and drift off into space.*

29. Motions of the planets. *A general layout of the solar system (central region enlarged) demonstrates the regularities of position and motion that must be explained by any theory of the origin of sun and planets. The arrows indicate that planets and asteroids all rotate about the sun in the same direction.*

great enough to cause it to fall past the edge of the earth. The stone will be in orbit. It is evident that the orbit is made possible by a balance between the speed of the stone and the attraction of the earth.

With air resistance present, the speed of the stone parallel to the earth's surface is continually being reduced. The balance between this speed and the earth's attraction is upset in favor of the earth's attraction and the stone spirals toward the earth.

If the stone is given more speed parallel to the earth's surface than it needs to balance the earth's attraction at that height, then its momentum will carry it farther away from the earth than it was when it started. This motion away from the earth will be slowed down by the earth's pull back toward the earth. If the initial speed is not too great, the earth's pull will eventually

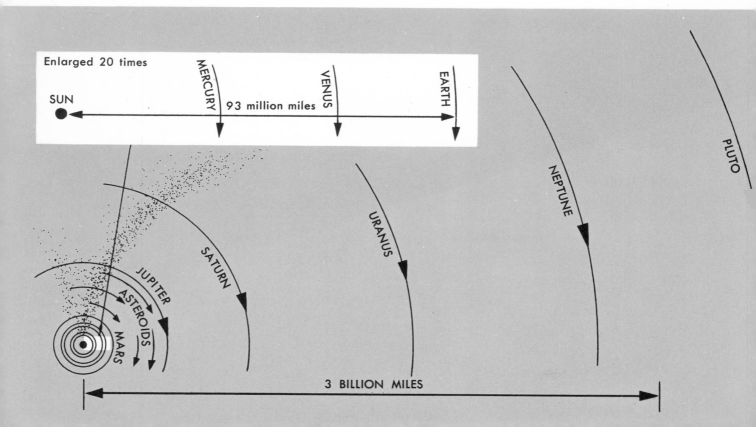

Enlarged 20 times

SUN

MERCURY

93 million miles

VENUS

EARTH

PLUTO

NEPTUNE

URANUS

SATURN

JUPITER

ASTEROIDS

MARS

3 BILLION MILES

cause the stone to turn about and fall back toward the earth. However, it will already have traveled so far away from the starting point that it will miss the earth in its fall and travel away from the earth again in the opposite direction. Again the earth will pull it back and the cycle will be repeated over and over. This is an elliptical orbit.

If the speed with which the stone travels away from the earth is great enough, the earth's attraction, decreasing as the stone soars higher and higher, will not be great enough to cause the stone to return. The stone will leave the earth forever.

The story of the stone is an imaginary one because air resistance prevents such orbits up to very great heights. If the necessary speed could be given the stone in air, the friction would create enough heat to melt the stone.

When an artificial satellite is launched from Cape Kennedy, the rocket must first be driven to an elevation where the air is very thin, usually over 100 miles high, before being given a burst of speed in a horizontal direction. As long as there is any air or gas or dust, the artificial satellite cannot stay up forever. It will slow down gradually and its path will curve down toward regions of increasing air density. The speed will decrease even more rapidly and the satellite will eventually burn up in the dense air or collide with the earth.

If a rocket is shot off with enough speed to escape from the earth without becoming an earth satellite, it will race along, free of the gravitational pull of the earth, subject only to the slight drag due to collisions with

30. Five planets visible to the naked eye. *Five planets are large and near enough to be seen with the unaided eye. As they appeared on the night of March 1, 1940, they were photographed in turn on the same film. From the horizon upward the planets are Mercury, Jupiter, Venus, Saturn (rings are discernible), and Mars.*

particles in space. Its occupants will feel weightless. The rocket will continue until it passes close enough to some heavenly body for the gravitational attraction to curve the path of flight. Actually, there is always some slight attraction, especially from the sun. If the path of flight passes near a planet, the rocket may become a satellite of that planet. Otherwise, it will

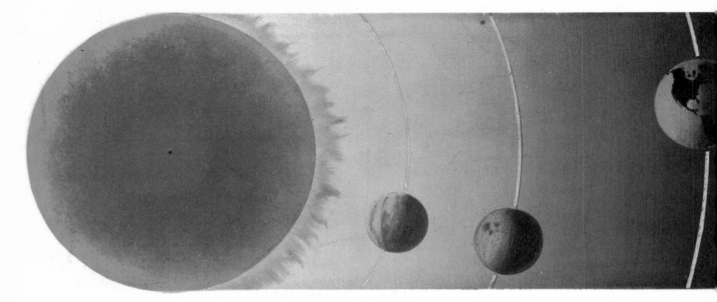

SUN   MERCURY   VENUS   EARTH

MERCURY 36

VENUS 67

EARTH 93

Distance from the sun in millions of miles

SUN   MARS 142   JUPITER 483   SATURN 1400   URANUS 1800

31. Why Mercury and Venus are invisible at night. *Mercury and Venus follow orbits between the earth and the sun. An astronomer scanning the skies from a part of the earth where night has fallen is looking away from the sun. Mercury and Venus lie behind him toward the sun and are therefore absent from the night sky.*

32. Groups in the planetary family. *The planets seem to be organized in natural groupings. Four small planets lie close to the sun: Mercury, Venus, Earth, and Mars. Four large planets lie at much greater distances: Jupiter, Saturn, Uranus, and Neptune. Pluto, about half the size of Earth, is the most distant planet and has a relatively long, narrow elliptic orbit.*

33. Venus is the morning or evening star. *Since Venus orbits between earth and sun, it is often hidden behind the sun or in the sun's blinding light. At other times it is off to one side, leading or lagging the sun across the sky. It appears either in early dawn before the sun rises to obscure it, or just after sunset. It is the brightest star of the morning or evening sky.*

NEPTUNE 2790   PLUTO 3670

become a weakly held satellite of the sun, similar to what we call a *planetoid*.

Something like this actually happens to some of the air particles in the atmosphere that clings to the earth. The gravitational attraction of the earth for the air particles permits the earth to hug the blanket of air about itself. The outermost particles of air, however, are so far away that the force of gravity holds them only loosely. As the earth rushes along in its race around the sun, it leaves behind some of this air. The air trails the earth like a wispy fringe (figure 28). Particles of air thus freed will drift about in space until they are captured by the gravitational pull of some heavenly body large enough or near enough to do so.

The Planetary Family Starting with the planet closest to the sun and proceeding according to increasing distance, the planets are Mercury, Venus, Earth, Mars, Jupiter, Saturn, Uranus, Neptune, and Pluto. With the exception of Earth, they are all named after ancient Greek or Roman gods. Between Mars and Jupiter are the many small planets, the planetoids (see figure 27). These are named after the lesser gods or even goddesses like Ceres, Pallas, and Vesta. Some of the smaller ones are considered so ungodlike, they are named after mere people like Victoria, Parthenope, Albert, and Eugenia, the wife of Napoleon III. Others have only numbers.

In figure 26 you can see a comparison of the sizes of the planets with that of the sun. A dot of ink could not be printed small enough to represent the planetoids. These baby planets range in size from a few miles to about 500 miles in diameter. If these seem like hardly noticeable rocks compared with the earth, remember that the earth does not look much bigger than this to a giant planet like Jupiter.

Figure 32 shows the planets arranged according to their distance from the sun. They seem to group themselves into two classes: four relatively small planets close to the sun and four large planets farther from the sun, with one planet left over. The four small planets are Mercury, Venus, Earth, and Mars. The large ones are Jupiter, Saturn, Uranus, and Neptune. The lonely outcast is Pluto, which is about half the size of the earth and is the most distant planet from the sun.

Notice that Mercury and Venus have orbits that lie between the earth and the sun (figure 31). For this reason we can never see them at night. When night reaches our part of the earth, the sun is behind us, shining on the opposite hemisphere. Since we are facing away from the sun, we are also facing away from Mercury and Venus. During the day, when we are facing the sun, Mercury and Venus can pass before us. However, there is so much light from the sun that the two little white spots are as invisible as two teardrops in the ocean. They appear only at dawn and at dusk when the sunlight is dim and indirect. Venus is the brightest star of morning and evening (figure 33) and has inspired beautiful poetry and music. The ancient Romans could not imagine that the star appearing at twilight

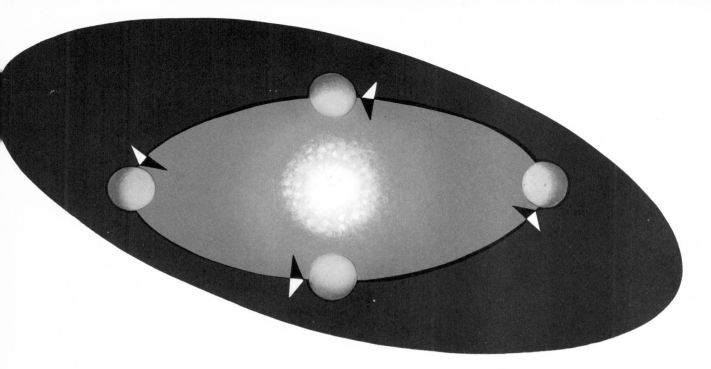

and the star that greeted them at dawn were one and the same. They were completely ignorant of the manner in which the planets revolved. As a result, they named the morning star Lucifer and the evening star Esperus.

Between Mars, the farthest of the small planets from the sun, and Jupiter, the first of the large planets, there lies the crowd of planetoids. The easily visible planets like Mercury, Venus, and Mars have been known since the remotest past, since man first recorded his vision of the heavens. The first of the planetoids to be discovered,

34. Motions of Mercury. *Mercury turns once on its axis for each revolution about the sun. As a result, it always presents approximately the same half of its surface to the sun. This side is hot enough to melt lead while the dark side has a temperature hundreds of degrees below zero.*

35. Relative sizes of Earth and Mercury. *Mercury has less than one half the diameter of Earth, about one twentieth as much mass, and only about one third as much gravitational attraction at its surface. A 200-pound Earthman who could survive the extremes of heat and cold would weigh about 67 pounds on Mercury.*

Ceres, was spied only in 1801 by the Italian astronomer, Piazzi.

Jupiter is the largest of all the planets in the solar system. If Jupiter were a planetary hotel, it could easily accommodate 300

36. Venus, in blue light. *Venus has phases like the moon's in which varying amounts of the surface are illuminated to a viewer on earth. Photographs made with different wave lengths or colors of light indicate that the visible details of Venus are not of the planet itself but of an enveloping cloud cover. Behind the veil of its atmosphere, Venus is still mysterious. Even its speed of rotation is not well known.*

earths as guests without overcrowding. Saturn is somewhat smaller than Jupiter, but still commands our respect. If all the other planets, except Jupiter, could be crammed together into a single, immense ball, it would take about five such balls to fill Saturn, Uranus and Neptune, the last of the group of large planets, are somewhat more moderate in size. They are still about 64 times the size of the earth.

The last planet, Pluto, is an odd planet. It is distinguished because it is farthest from the sun and probably has the greatest

density of all the planets. In many respects, however, it does not fit the pattern of the other planets. For example, in size it falls within the same group as the earth, but in position it is more related to the second group of larger planets.

Discovery of the Satellites
Until the beginning of the seventeenth century, astronomers were restricted to observing only what was visible to the naked eye. By this time crude telescopes began to appear. Part of the fame of Galileo Galilei, professor of

mathematics at the University of Padua in Italy, lay in the improved telescopes he constructed.

On the evening of January 7, 1610, Galileo focused his telescope on Jupiter. He was surprised to see not only the great planet itself, but also four small spots ro-

37. Earth-lit new moon. *At the time of the new moon, the moon is between the earth and sun and presents its unilluminated face to the earth. Only the thin bright crescent at the left reflects light arriving directly from the sun. The other visible details are lit by light reflected from the earth.*

Mercury	Venus	Earth	Mars	Jupiter	Saturn	Uranus	Neptune	Pluto
0	0	1	2	12	9	5	2	0

38. The planets. *Shown in order of distance from the sun with number of known satellites.*

tating about it, "like butterflies around a flame." Thus were discovered the first four satellites of Jupiter, the first moons to be seen, aside from our own.

Further examination of the skies over the years since Galileo's time disclosed that Jupiter had a total of 12 moons and that other planets also had satellites. A list of the planets is shown below in the order of their distance from the sun, together with the number of their satellites found so far.

If we combine this list with the representation of the planets shown in figure 32, we note that there seems to be a pattern in the arrangement of planetary sizes and the number of their satellites. Planets closer to the sun tend to be small and have few satellites or none at all. Planets farther from the sun tend to be larger and have more satellites. Only Pluto appears to be an exception to the general rule.

This pattern is unlikely to be just a coincidence. Any theory of how the solar system came to be formed must account for these facts.

A Closer Look at the Planets We are acquainted with the force of gravitation which steers the planets and satellites along their heavenly highways. We have been introduced to the planets by name. We have also noted some of their outstanding characteristics. Now let us start on our own imaginary journey and tour from planet to planet. We will start with the planet closest to the sun, Mercury. Be

thankful that the trip is only imaginary. You will discover that Mercury is not a place where you would want to live.

Since we have raised this question of living on other planets, let us keep it in mind. As we pay our visits, let us ask whether or not life is even possible on planets other than earth.

Mercury Mercury is not only closest to the sun, it is also the smallest of all the planets. Its diameter of about 3000 miles is less than half that of the earth (figure 35). If Mercury were sitting on the middle of the United States, its shadow would just about cover the country, from the Atlantic to the Pacific.

Mercury was named after the messenger of the ancient Roman gods. He had wings on his feet for swiftness. The planet Mercury, too, is swift. Our year on the earth is 365 days long because it takes the earth this time to make one complete circuit around the sun. Mercury completes its revolution about the sun in only 88 of our days. With this very short year, a boy who is 16 years old on earth would be 66 Mercury years old.

39. Close-up of the moon. *Large telescopes bring the moon close to us and the absence of an atmosphere makes the images very sharp. Fine details of the surface have been mapped and measured, including mountain ranges, craters, ridges, cracks, broad plains, and mysterious lines or rays that radiate from certain areas like the spokes of a wheel. A plain is named a mare (Latin for sea) because Galileo mistook the plains for oceans.*

52

A day is the time it takes the earth to spin once about its own axis. The earth spins 365 times to every one, sweeping excursion about the sun. Therefore, night and day alternate 365 times each year. As Mercury moves around the sun, at a distance of 36,000,000 miles, it rotates on its axis just once, according to some astronomers. If so, the planet always presents the same half of its surface to the sun. It is always the same day (or night). Also, Mercury is less than half as far as the earth from the sun and consequently receives 7 times as much heat and light on each square mile as does an equal area on earth. For this reason, on the half of Mercury where there may be eternal day, temperatures may exceed 660°F. On the night face they may be hundreds of degrees below zero. However, some observers believe that Mercury is actually spinning rapidly and the temperatures are not so extreme, the entire surface being warmed by the sun.

Either way, Mercury's temperatures are too severe to support life. Moreover, Mercury is too small to hold an atmosphere by gravitational attraction the way the earth does.

Venus Venus was the goddess of beauty. This name was given to the planet because at sunrise and sunset it is like a bright jewel in the sky. Venus is almost the same size as the earth, slightly smaller in diameter by about 200 miles. Like the earth, it has an atmosphere, but one quite different from ours. It is almost entirely carbon dioxide. In this gas are suspended a great many

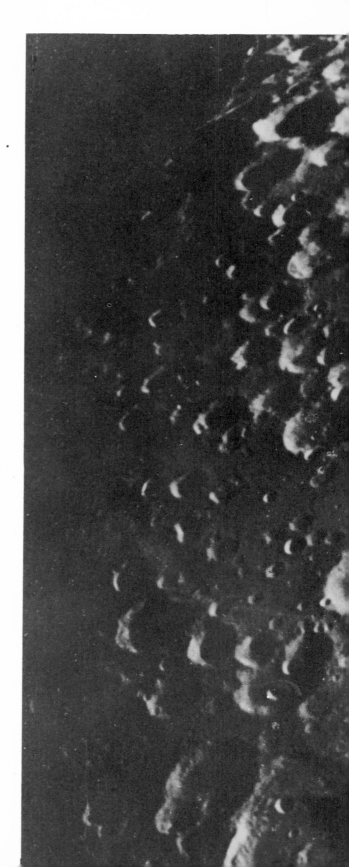

40. Craters on the moon. *The origin of the pock-marks on the moon is still in dispute. They are variously said to be the scars of meteorite impacts or remains of volcanoes. At lower right is the* crater Tycho, *about 54 miles across, more than 12,000 feet deep, and with a sharp peak rising from its center to a height of over 5000 feet. Total area shown is approximately 650 x 500 miles.*

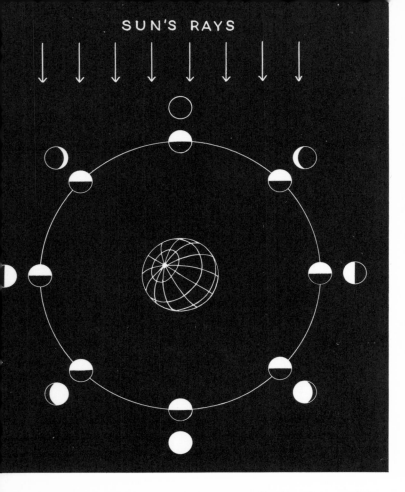

particles like a heavy dust. This wraps Venus in a thick layer of white clouds, completely obscuring the surface of the planet from our view. We do not even know of what the particles in this cloud consist.

Venus, at 67,000,000 miles, is much farther from the sun than Mercury. It is very hot, however, with a temperature as high as 800°F, according to the most recent measurements. Such an environment is not congenial to life. It is the very high temperature combined with the almost total lack of oxygen and the abundance of carbon dioxide in the atmosphere which make us think that there is no life as we know it on Venus.

41. Phases of the moon. *During the month-long cycle of the moon, it travels once around the earth. The face toward the sun is always illuminated, as represented by the moons on the white circle. At each position, or phase, however, an observer on earth sees a different amount of the illuminated portion. The outer ring of moons shows the appearance of the moon at each phase.*

FROM LEFT TO RIGHT:

42. Three-day-old moon. *The moon is almost new. The sun is on the far side of the moon, just barely to one side.*

43. Five-day-old moon. *The visible crescent is becoming thicker as the moon moves off to one side from between earth and sun.*

44. Sixteen-day-old moon. *The moon is just past being full. Full moon occurs at mid-cycle when the sun lies behind the earth and fully illuminates the side of the moon facing the earth.*

56

The Earth and the Moon We have already described a number of the features of the earth in comparing other planets with it. The earth revolves about the sun once a year at a distance of 93,000,000 miles. It turns about its own axis once every 24 hours. The earth has only one satellite, the moon, about 240,000 miles away from the parent body.

The moon has a diameter of approximately 2200 miles, about one-fourth that of the earth. Its volume is only one-fiftieth of the earth's.

Probably no movie actress has been photographed as often or as lovingly as the moon. Every surface feature visible on the moon has been mapped carefully and given a name. There are mountains, walls, great flat plains that look like dry oceans, and many craters. Figure 45 is an imaginative drawing of what the surface of the moon might look like to a visiting space traveler.

There is some dispute as to the nature and origin of the moon craters. Some scientists feel that they were formed by volcanoes erupting on the moon just as they do on earth. However, volcanic craters on earth are no more than about 8 miles across. Those on the moon are as large as 93 miles across. Others feel that the craters are holes caused by the collisions of meteorites with the moon. The walls of the craters are the material splashed up from the hole. Recent evidence favors the meteorite theory.

Just as Mercury always presents the same face to the sun, the moon always shows the same face to the earth. The reasons are the same. The moon makes a complete revolution about the earth in approximately 28 days. As it does so, it rotates about itself in the same direction, and also completes this rotation in the same time. The moon and the earth are like two wrestlers. One circles warily about the other, always turning to face his opponent, as if to prevent a surprise attack. Because of this, we on earth never see the other side of the moon. Only recently a Russian rocket with a camera was sent around the moon to photograph the far side. The image transmitted back to the earth showed what everyone expected. The other side of the moon looks very much like this one.

The moon, like Mercury, is too small to provide the gravitational pull necessary to hold an atmosphere. If man ever succeeds in an expedition to the moon, he will have to carry his own oxygen supply. He might have to wear a suit very much like the one worn by the space traveler in figure 45.

The moon is responsible for two important occurrences that affect the earth: *eclipses* and *tides*. Figures 48 and 50 show how the two kinds of eclipses come about. In a lunar eclipse, the earth lies in line between the moon and the sun and throws its shadow over the moon. In a solar eclipse, the moon comes between the sun and the earth. Because the moon is so much smaller than the earth, it does not block all the sun's light from reaching the earth. It can only cast a dark patch on the earth, the way

a small cloud does when it floats over an otherwise sunny landscape. People within the shadow cannot see the sun just as people under the cloud find the sun blotted out. However, people elsewhere will see only a partial eclipse or, if they are at point *A* in figure 50, they will see no eclipse at all.

The movements of the sun, earth, and moon are well known now. Therefore, astronomers can predict exactly when eclipses will occur. More than that, they can calculate exactly when they must have occurred in the past. This has served some interesting, non-astronomical purposes. For example, in an account of a battle between two ancient peoples, the Lydians and the Medes, the Greek historian, Herodotus, mentioned that the fighters stopped because they were awed by a total eclipse of the sun. In fact, this ended the war. For a long time, later historians were uncertain about the date of the battle. They could estimate only that it must have happened between 626 and 538 B.C. The astronomers calculated that the only such eclipse that occurred about that time took place on May 28 of the year 585 B.C. Thus, the astronomers were able to tell the historians the exact date of the battle.

From earliest times superstitious people have been in terror of eclipses. Superstition

45. The earth as it might appear from the moon. *In the near future a space expedition may very well bring back actual photographs of such a journey. Since the earth's diameter is 4 times that of the moon, it will loom larger to moon men in their sky than the moon does in our sky.*

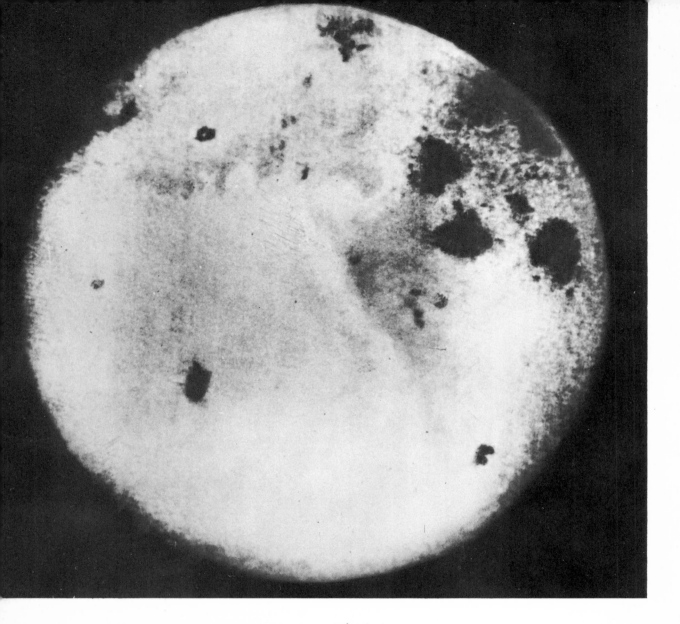

46. Reverse side of the moon. *An image of the back side of the moon was transmitted by radio waves to earth from the Soviet space vehicle, Lunik III. The apparent scarcity of craters may not be real. The moon was full and direct sunlight may have eliminated shadows, causing a flat appearance. In 1962, the United States' vehicle Ranger 4 was reported to have landed on the reverse side of the moon.*

47. Total eclipse of the moon. *The earth blocks the light from the sun behind it and casts a shadow over the moon before it. The moon is visible because sunlight passing around the earth is bent (refracted) by the atmosphere into the region of shadow. Blue light is filtered out by the atmosphere, giving the eclipsed moon a reddish tint. Sunsets are red for the same reason.*

60

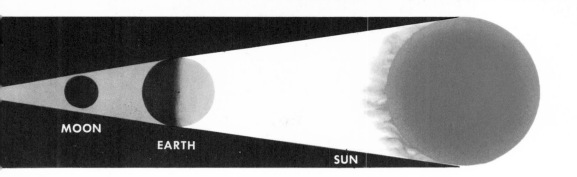

48. Eclipse of the moon. *When the earth lies directly between the sun and the moon, the moon is completely within the earth's shadow. As the three bodies approach these positions, observers on the dark side of the earth see the edge of the shadow progress across the moon, gradually obscuring it and then revealing it again.*

49. Partial eclipse of the moon. *When only part of the moon dips into the earth's shadow, the result is a partial lunar eclipse. The moon was photographed at five-minute intervals as the earth turned. It is the turning of the earth that makes the moon appear to rise.*

50. Eclipse of the sun. *When the moon lies directly between the sun and the earth, it casts a shadow over part of the earth. Depending on the relative distances among earth, moon, and sun, which vary, an observer in the shadow may see a total eclipse or an annular eclipse. In a total eclipse, the entire body of the sun is hidden, showing only the fiery corona. In an annular eclipse, an outer ring remains visible.*

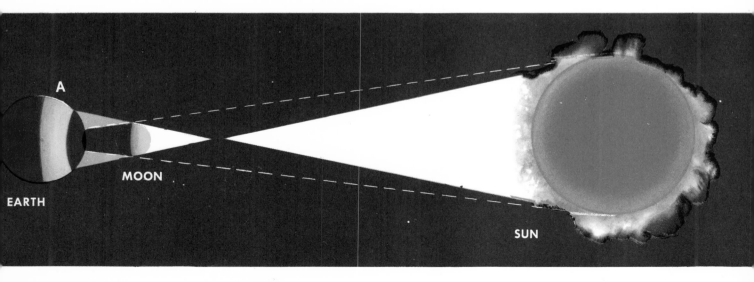

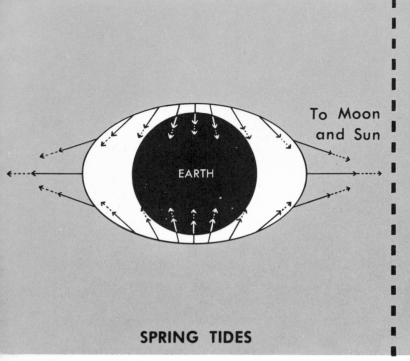

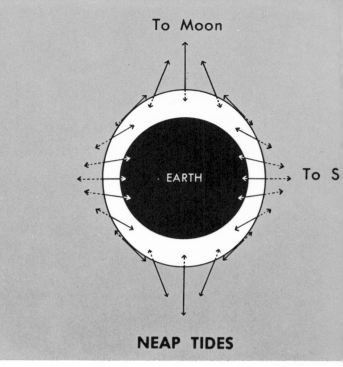

SPRING TIDES

NEAP TIDES

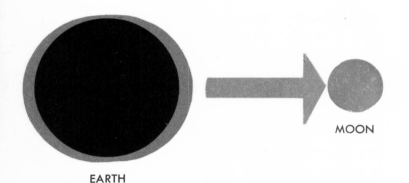

MOON

EARTH

51. Principal cause of tides. *Oceans, a watery jacket covering most of the earth, are drawn toward the moon by its gravitational pull, rising to high tide in the region of earth closest to the moon. Opposite this region, distance weakens the moon's influence and waters there remain also at relatively high tide levels. Midway there is a belt of low tide, partially emptied by the outward flow.*

a   *b*   *c*

is usually based on ignorance. In their ignorance, the frightened people thought the sun was being stolen and might never return. During the eclipse of May 15, 1877, mobs in Turkey rioted from fear. They ran through the streets shouting insanely that the sun was being eaten by a dragon. To free the sun from the talons of the monster, they shot their guns wildly toward the sky. Only with knowledge and understanding do people now accept eclipses calmly. They no longer dread the possibility of eternal darkness and bitter cold that the disappearance of the sun seemed to threaten.

Eclipses caused terror because they seldom happened and seemed to disrupt the natural course of events. Tides were not fearsome because they were common, everyday happenings. Their regular com-

52. Daily cycle of tides. *In 24 hours the earth carries a point* (p) *on its surface full circle around to its starting position relative to the moon. The point passes through alternating tidal conditions, two high tides and two low tides each day.*

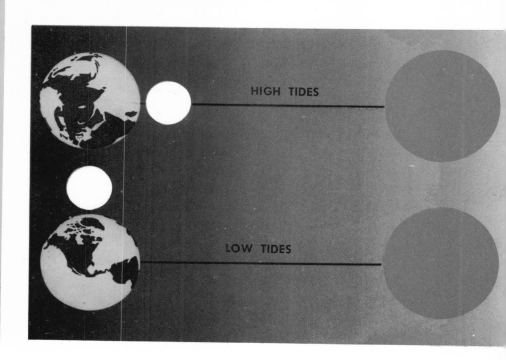

53. Spring tides and neap tides. *Tides are affected by the sun but only to a small extent because of its great distance from the earth. When earth, moon, and sun are in line, tidal forces of the sun (dashed arrows) add to moon forces (solid arrows) and spring tides occur. High tides are higher than usual, low tides lower. Neap, or diminished, tides occur when sun tides and moon tides conflict.*

HIGH TIDES

LOW TIDES

ing and going was almost a comforting symbol of an orderly rhythm in nature. Yet, tides were a perplexing puzzle to people of earlier times.

Almost three-quarters of our earth is submerged beneath the sea. The sea varies in depth from the shallow places near shore, where we swim, to over six miles straight down. This extreme depth was measured at an underwater trench discovered beneath the Pacific Ocean near the Philippine Islands. It is as if one vast sea embraces the globe. From this sea there protrude great islands, which are the continents such as North America, Europe, Africa. Here and there other islands raise their crowns above the water. These are smaller and range in size from islands like Madagascar or the Hawaiian and Philippine groups, down to little islets and sea rocks. Above this water-covered globe the moon circles, exerting its gravitational pull. The attraction is greatest at the point on earth nearest the moon. Since the water is fluid,

it can flow in response to the pull of the moon. The solid portions of the earth may stir a little, like a heavy dough, but cannot flow like water.

The drawing in figure 51 simplifies the manner in which tides are produced. Sea waters on the side of the earth facing the moon flow toward the moon. This raises the water level immediately under the moon and lowers it in the regions from which water has departed. Sea waters on the opposite side of the earth are more distant from the moon. Therefore, they are attracted much less and tend to remain where they are. The result is high tides on two regions of the earth and low tides midway between these two regions.

However, the earth is not standing still but rotates about its center once every 24 hours. Thus, a new part of the earth is always coming into position beneath the moon. The region of high tide then appears at this new part of the earth. In figure 52a, for example, point p on earth is in a region

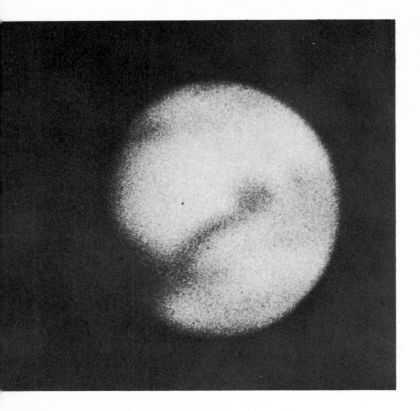

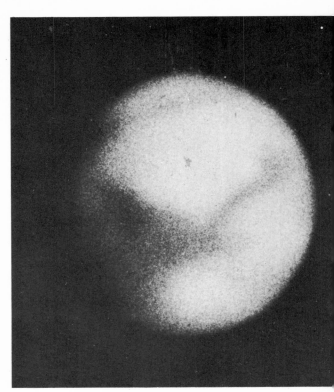

54-57. Rotation of Mars. *In 54, 55, and 56 the planet Mars was photographed with red light which reveals surface markings. Rotation is clearly indicated by the progression of the markings across the surface. 57 was taken with blue light and lacks detail but emphasizes the polar cap.*

of low tide. One-quarter of a day, or 6 hours later, the earth has made a quarter of a turn about. This is represented by figure 52b in which point *p* has been carried into a region of high tide. ·Six hours after that the earth has made another quarter turn and *p* is again in a region of low tide as in figure 52c. After another 6 hours and another quarter turn *p* will again have a high tide. After a full day of 24 hours, the point *p* will be back where it started from in figure 52a, again at low tide. That is why during a 24-hour period a point on the sea experiences two high tides and two low tides.

The gravitational attraction of the sun also plays a part in tides. Big as the sun is, it is also very far away. Its influence on tides is, therefore, much less than that of the moon. Depending on its position in the sky, the sun increases or decreases the height of the tides. In figure 53, we can see that when the sun is on the same side of the earth as the moon, their gravitational forces are combined. The high tide is higher. When the sun is pulling at right angles to the moon, as in the second illustration of figure 53, the tides are diminished. For other positions of the sun relative to the moon, their effects neither add completely nor subtract completely. The influence of the sun may appear as a shift in the time high tide occurs at any particular place. It may advance or delay the hour of full tide depending on the positions of moon and sun.

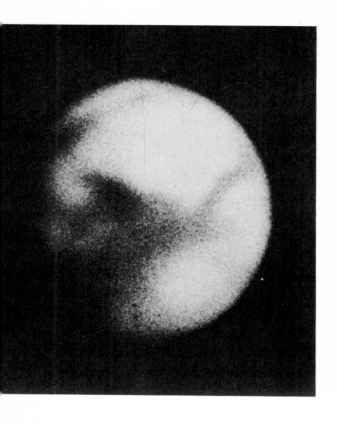

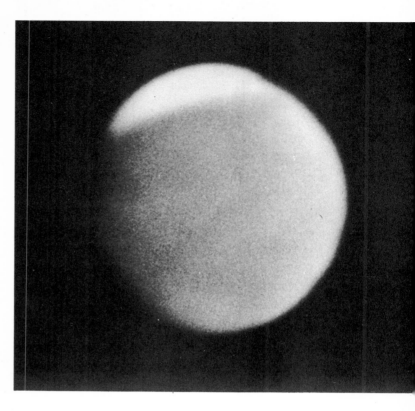

The appearance of tides can be very dependent on the shape of the coastal land. Where there is a gently sloping, flat beach, a bather who falls asleep at the water's edge at high tide may awake at low tide to find that the sea seems to have disappeared. Actually, in falling a few feet in level, the retreating waters may uncover a vast expanse of beach. On the other hand, in the Bay of Fundy in Canada, tidal waters come rushing through a narrow channel at a very swift pace. From low to high tide the water may rise up to 70 feet in some parts. This can happen so rapidly that there are signs on the beach warning swimmers not to fall asleep on the shore.

We will continue our discussion of the planet Earth later in the book. Now, let us make another giant leap to the next stop on our tour of the planets—the red planet, Mars.

Mars   Mars has a reddish color, which probably led to its being named after the bloodthirsty god of war of ancient Rome. It is thought that an abundance of iron oxide (a form of rust) in the soil causes this color.

Mars is about one-half as large as the earth, with a diameter of almost 4300 miles. It is 142,000,000 miles from the sun, so the intensity of the sun's rays on Mars is not as great as on earth. Mars differs from earth also in that it has a somewhat lower density. Despite these differences, there are enough similarities for Mars sometimes to be considered a smaller brother of earth.

There appear to be something like our north and south poles on Mars. These have the form of two white icecaps which grow larger in winter, shrink in summer, and sometimes almost vanish completely. It

58. Jupiter dwarfs the earth. *Jupiter is the giant of the planetary family with a volume about 1320 times that of the earth. Jupiter and its 12 moons take almost 12 earth years to complete a revolution around the sun at an average distance of 484,000,000 miles.*

59, 60. Two views of Jupiter. *Jupiter, the largest planet, is as heavy as all other planets put together and has the most satellites, 12 moons in all. Below, one moon casts its shadow on the bright disk of*

takes Mars almost twice as long to circle about the sun as the year required by the earth. But day and night alternate in a 24½-hour cycle very much like ours. Moreover, Mars has an atmosphere and even some clouds. If it has all this, could Mars have people?

If we look closely, we see that human beings would find Mars generally uninhabitable under present conditions. The atmosphere is very thin and does not contain the

Jupiter. At right, rotation has moved the shadow and brought the moon itself into view (bright spot to right). Little is known of Jupiter's interior because it is hidden by thick bands of clouds.

oxygen or water vapor we require. The atmosphere is probably almost entirely nitrogen. Mars has day and night, winter and summer, but the temperature changes are not as gentle as those on earth. Without a thick blanket of atmosphere to shield it from the sun and to provide insulation against heat loss from the surface of the planet, Mars has a severe climate. When the sun disappears at night or grows more distant during winter, Mars cools off rapidly. The average temperature, about which there are wide fluctuations, is around 22°F below zero. Compare this with our normal temperature which averages about 50 to 60°F above zero.

The water shortage would be a severe problem for any inhabitants. There is none in the atmosphere as there is in ours. Mars has some water locked up as ice in the icecaps. However, the icecaps must be extremely thin since they melt completely during summer. They may not be true icecaps at all, but only layers of frost. The water supply is therefore quite undependable.

Although conditions on Mars are certainly not favorable for living creatures, some form of life may be possible. For

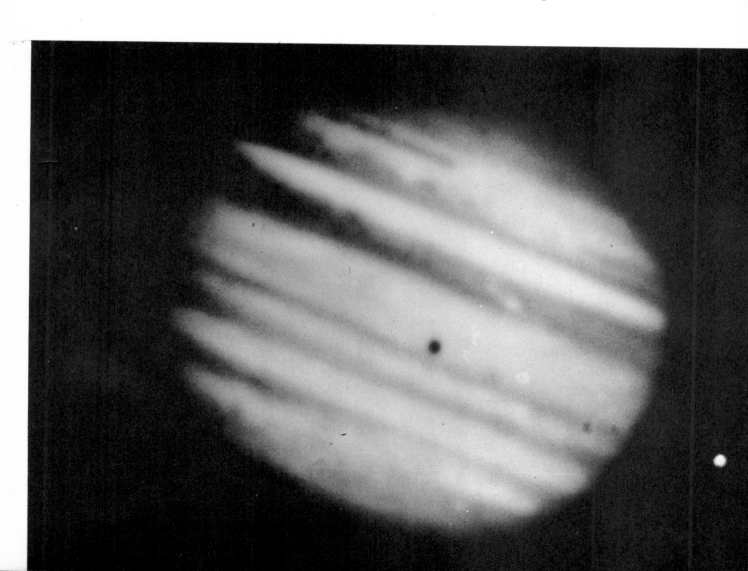

approximately 300 years, grayish-green patches have been observed on Mars. These patches change color from time to time and suggest that there may be some kind of vegetation growing in these areas. Because we have on earth a tough, primitive plant which could survive on Mars, it now seems likely that a plant of this type actually does grow there. This family of plants is the lichen. They live on very little water and can withstand extremely low temperatures. A short immersion in liquid air at almost 300° F below zero does not kill them. They are found in the Sahara Desert, in dark caves, and clinging to bare rocks on the tops of our highest mountains. They seem able to live on chalk or lime. Another extremely hardy plant family on earth includes the mosses. It is reasonable to assume that, if there is any life on Mars, it is probably some form of lichen or moss.

If there were inhabitants on Mars, and if these inhabitants were at all romantic, they could enjoy the two moons that light the night sky. However, these moons were not given romantic names. They were named after the war horses of the fierce warrior god. One is Phobos, which means fear. The other is Deimos, which means terror.

Jupiter We will skip the planetoids scattered through the space beyond Mars. This brings our tour to the giant of the planetary family, Jupiter. Among the Roman gods, Jupiter was the greatest of all. This largest of planets is so much farther from the sun than we on earth are, that it takes twelve times as long for it to complete its wide swing around the sun. This means its year is twelve times as long as ours. Jupiter is 483,000,000 miles from the sun.

Remember the boy who was 16 years old on earth but was 66 Mercury years old? On Jupiter his age would be considered less than a year and a half.

This does not mean that Jupiter is a slow giant. In spite of a diameter of 89,000 miles, over ten times that of the earth, Jupiter performs its daily turnabout in less than 10 hours. That is only 5 hours of day and 5 hours of night. A point on the rim of this huge spinning ball is whipped along at a speed of about 30,000 miles per hour. A point on the equator of the earth moves a little over 1000 miles per hour as the earth spins from night to day.

A visitor to Jupiter will not find any natives coming out to greet him. The surface layers of the planet are mainly unbreathable gases composed of hydrogen and hydrogen compounds. Jupiter's average density is less than that of the sun. Moreover, with an outer temperature of about 150°F below zero, this is not a place where one may expect to find life.

Night on Jupiter might be a splendid sight, with twelve moons to shine at various times like lanterns at a garden party. The four moons discovered by Galileo are of course the largest and most easily seen from earth. Two, Ganymede and Callisto, are bigger than Mercury. The smallest is barely 12 miles in diameter. Besides its distinction as the largest planet and the possessor of the most moons, Jupiter is also

61. Saturn and ring system. *With its nine satellites and unique rings, Saturn has a special beauty among the planets. It is also one of the larger planets and the most distant planet known before the eighteenth century. The bands on the central globe are clouds of ammonia crystals lengthened into continuous belts by the rapid rotation about the axis.*

the source of some mysterious radio signals, discovered several years ago by radio astronomers and still being interpreted.

Saturn Galileo, pleased with the discovery of Jupiter's satellites, naturally turned his new telescope toward Saturn. He sensed there was something strange about Saturn, but the image was not clear. At first he thought he saw two satellites nearby, but could not find them the next time he looked. He became discouraged and gave up.

Nine years later, a great Dutch physicist,

Christian Huygens, studied Saturn with a more powerful telescope. He reported his discovery in the following manner:

aaaaa,ccccc,d,eeeee,g,h,iiiiii,lll,mm,
nnnnnnnn,oooo,p,q,rr,s,ttttt,uuuuu

This was an exasperating habit of the times. Galileo, too, had made public his observations in the form of such a puzzle. These puzzles were anagrams. The letters or words had to be unscrambled and put together in the proper way to decipher the statement. Huygens waited three years before publishing the solution to his anagram. It was in Latin:

Annulo cingitur tenuo, nusquam
coherente, ad eclipticam inclinato.

In translation, this says, "It is surrounded by a thin ring, which never touches it, inclined upon the ecliptic."

What this means is that Huygens had discovered the rings of Saturn. Huygens thought there was just one flat ring which circled the mid-section of Saturn like the brim of a cowboy's hat. Modern telescopes have shown that there is really a series of rings, each of different brightness. The rings have varying diameters so that the smaller rings nest within the larger ones, as shown in figure 61. For the smallest ring, the inner edge is about 7000 miles from the surface of the planet. The outer edge of the largest ring is almost 50,000 miles from Saturn itself. The main body of Saturn has a diameter of some 75,000 miles. This brings the outside diameter of the outermost ring to about 172,000 miles.

These rings make Saturn one of the most beautiful sights visible through a telescope. They are less than 10 miles thick and seem to be composed of swarms of small particles like dust.

In addition to its rings, Saturn is escorted by nine moons as it revolves about the sun at a distance of 1,400,000,000 miles. That is almost one and one-half billion miles. As our tour takes us to the more distant planets, the number of zeros is becoming truly impressive. Because it is so far from the sun, Saturn is chilled for lack of heat and light. It gets only one-ninetieth as much as we do.

Saturn is the least dense of all the planets. Its material is so loosely packed that it is the only planet that would float on water.

Like Jupiter, Saturn has a long year—about 30 earth years. Also like Jupiter, Saturn has a short day. This planet rotates about itself in 10 hours and 38 minutes.

All in all, Saturn is a special curiosity among the planets because of its rings and moons and remarkably light mass for its size.

Uranus For many years Saturn was considered the last of the planets in terms of distance from the sun. The idea became so fixed, that people could not even imagine that there might be more planets. Therefore, when Sir William Herschel and his sister Caroline discovered Uranus in 1781, they were not bold enough to contradict

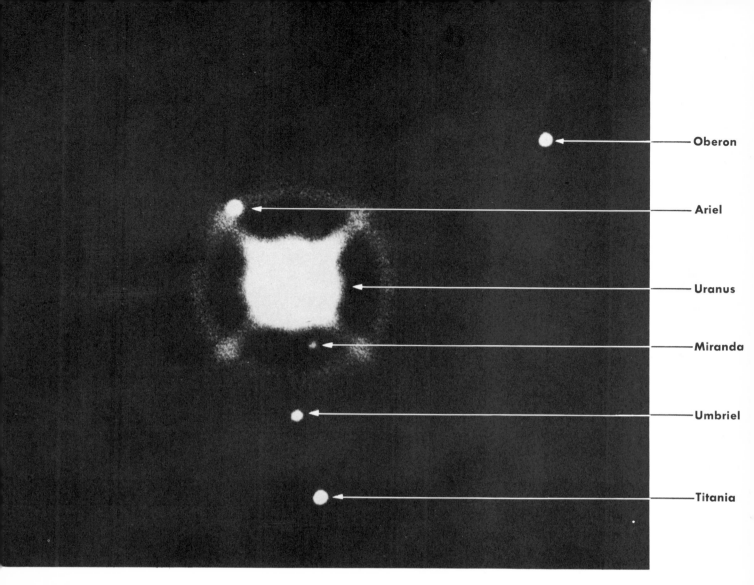

— Oberon

— Ariel

— Uranus

— Miranda

— Umbriel

— Titania

62. Uranus and satellite system. *The third largest planet is barely visible to the naked eye because of its distance from earth. Through a telescope it is a greenish blur, its surface details obscured by its atmosphere. All five known moons can be seen in the photograph. The fifth, discovered only in 1948, is the dim white spot within the halation ring caused by reflections within the telescope.*

public opinion. Herschel announced that they had discovered a new comet. But Uranus stubbornly refused to act like a comet. Astronomers were compelled to extend the dimensions of the solar system to accommodate the new planet. Uranus is almost 1,800,000,000 miles from the sun, over one and one-half billion miles.

Uranus is just about four times as big as the earth. Its diameter is approximately 30,000 miles.

As it swings around the sun, Uranus, like the other planets, also rotates about itself. The *axis* of rotation of a planet is the imaginary line that goes through the center of the globe, from north pole to south pole, about which the planet turns like a roast on a barbecue spit. There is something odd about the axis of rotation of Uranus.

Consider how the earth turns. If we imagine the sun to be a large stationary ball on a great flat table, the earth is a spinning top which circles about the sun as it spins

THE SEASONS ON EARTH

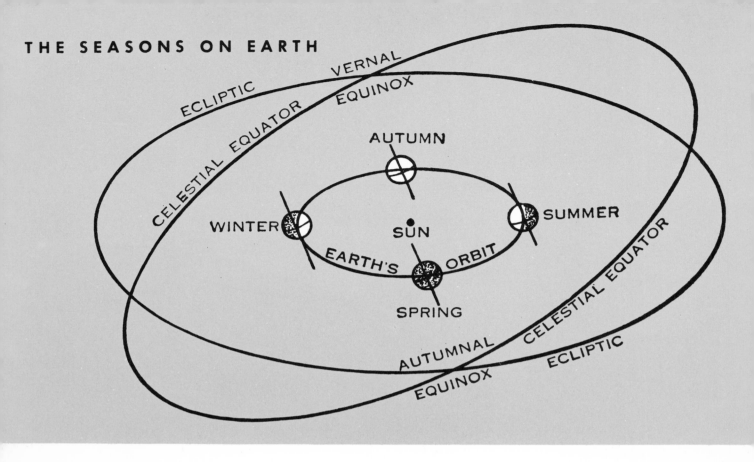

63. Cause of our seasons. *The tilt of the earth's axis brings one hemisphere closer to the sun and the other hemisphere farther away, warming the first to summer, cooling the second to winter. Half a year later, the earth has circled to the other side of the sun and the situation is reversed. Midway, the axis points neither toward nor away from the sun. Both hemispheres have the medium temperatures of spring or autumn. The ecliptic is the circle in which the plane of the earth's orbit cuts an imaginary celestial sphere. The celestial equator is tilted from the ecliptic by the same angle as the earth's axis. The two points of intersection of these circles are the equinoxes which mark the positions of the earth at the change of seasons.*

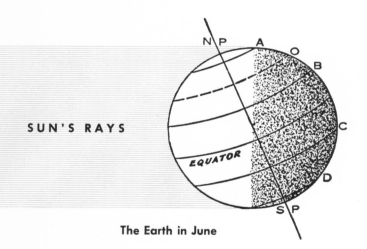

SUN'S RAYS

The Earth in June

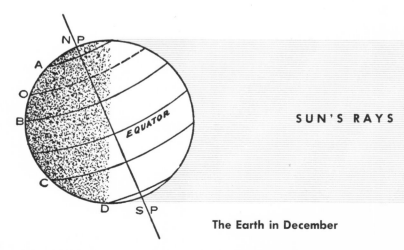

SUN'S RAYS

The Earth in December

on the table. The axis of rotation of the earth is not quite straight up from the table, but is tilted a bit off the vertical. As the spinning earth revolves about the sun, sometimes its axis is tilted with the upper end toward the sun. When this happens the upper part of the earth is closer to the sun and the summer season begins. At other times, the upper end of the axis is tilted away from the sun. Then the upper part of the earth cools and the winter season begins. The lower half is tilted toward the sun and enjoys summer. Half of the year, one-half has winter and spring, the other summer and fall. The other half of the year, the conditions are reversed. After a whole year, the spinning top, which we are calling the earth, has come full circle about the sun and the cycle starts all over again.

The middle part of the earth, the equator, is always nearer the sun than the rest of the earth. Therefore, it has summer practically all year round.

With Uranus we have a different situation. Its axis of rotation is lying flat, parallel to the table, so the imaginary top is rolling on its side on our imaginary table. As the planet circles the sun, the axis does not just point in toward the sun all the time like the spoke of a wheel. Instead, at one time one end of the axis points toward the sun, at another time the other end points toward the sun. In between, the axis is in the process of swinging from one extreme position to the other. The ends of the axis are the north and south poles of Uranus. Summer comes to the north pole when its end of the axis points toward the sun like an arrow.

After summer and fall, the arrow has swung around and its tail, the south pole, points toward the sun. Now the north pole begins its winter and the south pole begins its summer. A Uranus year is 84 of our earth years. Each pole has a summer and fall 42 years long and then labors through a winter and spring just as long.

Uranus is interesting in another respect. It is the first planet we have visited from which the earth is invisible without the aid of a telescope. It is that far away from us. This is a blow to man's pride. For so many years man felt that he and his earth were the center of the universe. Now, he has found that not only does the earth rotate about the sun as one of many other planets, but for some of these planets earth does not even exist. At least this is true in the sense that an observer on Uranus or Neptune or Pluto (the two next planets) would not even see the earth as a dim star in the dark heavens.

Neptune We said earlier that Neptune was discovered because Uranus misbehaved. What happened was that an orbit was calculated for Uranus according to Newton's Law of Universal Gravitation. Up to about 1800, Uranus apparently followed that orbit. Then it seemed to swerve a bit. At first, there was only a slight difference and astronomers were not sure whether or not it was some error in their measurements. By 1840 Uranus was so far off course, there was no question about it. There was a choice of saying that Newton's Law was defective or of finding some other

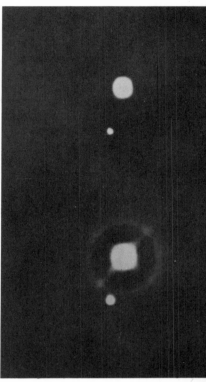

64, 65. Neptune and its two satellites. *At left, the fourth largest planet is a white blur almost covering its nearby moon, Triton, below it. The second moon (arrow) is Nereid, about 3.5 million miles away. At right, greater magnification produces more separation between Neptune and Triton in two photographs taken 11 minutes apart. Absence of other close satellites is clear.*

reason. According to this law, the only other reason could be that there was a large, still undiscovered body which was providing a gravitational pull not taken into account.

A young French mathematician by the name of Leverrier made a vast number of calculations. He patiently determined the influence of Saturn and Jupiter on the orbit of Uranus. This did not explain the new orbit of Uranus. By September, 1843, Leverrier had come to the conclusion that there must be a planet farther away from the sun than Uranus. Moreover, he said

that this planet could be found by looking at a particular angle in the sky.

Leverrier was so sure and calm about his calculations, he did not even rush to a telescope to search for his mystery planet. He waited almost a month before writing to an astronomer at the Berlin Observatory in Germany, asking the astronomer to look for the planet. On the night of September 23, the astronomer trained his telescope on the point described by Leverrier and discovered Neptune. The error in the angle described by the Frenchman was only one degree.

66. Relative sizes of Neptune and Earth. *Neptune is the farthest from the sun of the group of larger planets, at a distance of almost 3 billion miles. It is the first planet not visible to the unaided eye and could not be discovered until the invention of the telescope. The diameter of Neptune is three and one half times that of earth.*

67. The sun seen from various planets. *Impressions of the sun's size are often more psychological than mathematical. It seems bigger on a clear, hot day than on a dim, cloudy one. From nearby Mercury (1), the sun must seem almost to fill the sky although it occupies less than 2 degrees of angle. To Earth (2), it is the familiar orange ball. From far Neptune (3), it is a modest little glowing circle.*

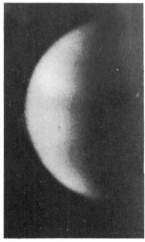
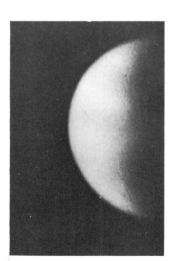

68. Pluto. *Unlike the other more distant planets, Pluto is relatively small, having about half the diameter of earth. Although known as the outermost planet of the solar system, its orbit is so eccentric that by 1989 Pluto will be closer to the sun than Neptune. The four views photographed over a period of one hour show increasing portions of illuminated surface, a product of the changing positions of earth, sun, and Pluto.*

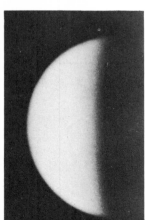
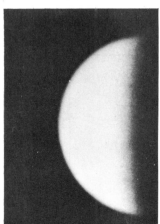

Neptune and Uranus are almost twins, both having diameters of about 30,000 miles. Figure 66 shows a comparison of the dimensions of Neptune and the earth. Of course, Neptune is even farther from the sun than Uranus, a distance of 2,790,000,000 miles. At such a distance Neptune has such a long way to go around the sun that its year is almost 165 times as long as that of the earth. There are two satellites of Neptune. The larger one, Triton, is actually not much smaller than the planet Mars.

When planets are as far from the sun as Uranus, Neptune, and the final planet, Pluto, there is so little warmth that life as we know it is inconceivable.

69. Orbit of a comet. *A comet follows an elliptical path as do the planets, but its ellipse is long and narrow with the sun near one end. Therefore the comet spends little time near the sun. It appears, swings around the sun, and vanishes toward the far end of its orbit. Some comets return in years, some in centuries, and some apparently never.*

Pluto With Pluto, history repeated itself. With more and more careful observations, it was found that Neptune did not explain all the erratic ways of Uranus. In 1915, the existence of still another planet was predicted. It took over 15 years to find this last and most distant planet. Only in 1931, with the aid of sensitive photographic equipment, was the planet Pluto found. The reason it had escaped the long search was that it was about half as large as the earth. At an average distance of 3,700,000,000 miles from the sun, it is not hard to overlook a pinpoint half the size of the earth.

Pluto, the last of the planets, revolves about the sun once every 248 earth years. It is distinguished in that it is the densest of all the planets. This small, dense body marches a lonely patrol at the remote borders of our solar system.

We have now finished our tour of the planets, but we are not quite ready to leave the solar system.

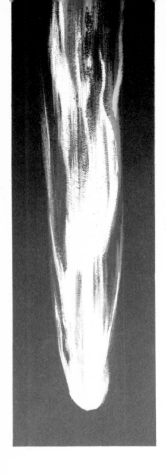

Comets Comets are strange bodies that appear suddenly in the heavens, and then disappear. Some reappear at certain intervals of time. Others have been seen only once.

The comets that return are called *periodic*. The period is the interval of time between two appearances. Some come back at intervals of only 3 years. Others stay away for thousands of years before returning. It used to be thought that comets with such long periods would never return. They were called *non-periodic*. It was suggested that they came from outer space, even beyond our solar system, made one swing around our sun, and then sped off forever. More accurate calculations indicate this is not true.

All comets travel in elliptical orbits be-

COMETS AND FALLING STARS

The solar family includes all bodies, large and small, that travel around the sun, guided by its gravitational influence. By this definition, we have not yet exhausted the list of family members. There are still the comets and the "falling stars." Comets are like beloved uncles who drop in, stay for a while, and then depart for distant places. "Falling stars," commonly known as meteors, are like broods of unruly children playing with their flashlights after bedtime.

70. Comet Morehouse. *This 1908 visitor to our skies wore a complex tail made up of sheet-like masses.*

cause their paths are governed by the gravitational attraction of the sun. However, these ellipses are long and thin compared with the orbits of the planets. The difference between the periodic and the so-called non-periodic comets is that the periodic comets have orbits that are very much shorter than those of the non-periodic comets. The periodic comets can race from one end of their orbits to the other and back in a reasonable time.

Near one end of the orbit of a comet lies the sun. The other end may be far out beyond the farthest planet, Pluto. When a comet approaches the sun, it becomes near enough for us to see it from the earth. It rounds the sun and speeds away again, out of sight. On the next trip back to the end of the orbit near the sun, it again comes into our view.

Kepler, the famous astronomer of Galileo's time, was once asked, "How many comets are there in space?" He replied, "As many as there are fishes in the ocean." This may be an overestimate. At least, up to the present time, only about one thousand comets have been discovered. Great as this number is, very few can be seen without a telescope. Most comets are watched only by astronomers. Just one periodic comet may be seen with the naked eye. This is Halley's comet, which always creates a good deal of public excitement when it arrives at its appointed time.

71. Arrival and departure of Halley's Comet. *During its last visit in 1910, Halley's Comet was photographed as thoroughly as any celebrity making a public appearance. In closest pictures, camera had to be moved to keep pace with the comet, causing fixed stars in background to leave star trails.*

| April 26 | April 27 | April 30 | May 2 | May 3 | May 4 | May 6 |

The Most Famous Comet Many comets pay us more frequent visits than Halley's. Encke's comet repeats its performance about every 3 years. We know of some twenty comets with periods between 5 and 10 years. Although Halley's comet takes three-quarters of a century to return, it is by far the best known.

It was named after Edmund Halley, an English astronomer, who was a friend and co-worker of Newton. In 1682 a brilliant comet made a dramatic entrance into the skies. While studying the motion of comets in general, Halley noticed that this comet of 1682 had a similar speed and path of travel to two other comets. These other comets had appeared, respectively, in 1531

72. Head of Halley's Comet. *The most famous of all comets presented this spectacular appearance in 1910. It was the first comet shown to have an elliptic orbit which permitted a calculation of the period of reappearance. It is expected next in 1986.*

May 15   May 23   May 28   June 3   June 6   June 9   June 11

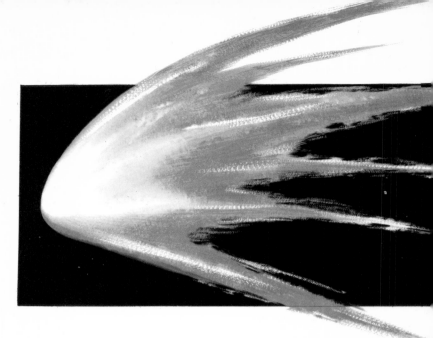

73. Six tails of the Comet of 1744.
The thin glowing particles of gas that form the tail streaming from the head of a comet often appear divided into a number of separate strands. The Comet of 1744 is a striking example of a many-tailed visitor from space.

and 1607. He suggested that the three might all be the same comet with a period of about 76 years. If so, the comet should reappear in 1758. This was the first time the return of a comet was predicted.

To pinpoint the date more exactly, two mathematicians worked for 6 months at exhausting calculations. When finished, they announced that the comet should return in the middle of April, 1759. They estimated that the possible error in their calculations was about one month.

Early in the year 1759, excitement ran high as the world awaited the coming of the comet. In those days, scientists were not necessarily as highly regarded as they are now. People were as likely to put more faith in the mumblings of a fortuneteller as in the careful computations of an astronomer. On March 12, 1759, the comet arrived, on course and on time. This was a magnificent verification of the observations and calculations of the astronomers, and of the gravitational theory of Newton.

There was now no doubt that the four comets were really one, as Halley had suggested. The comet was named in his honor.

Halley's comet has since kept to its schedule faithfully, having last appeared in 1910. We are looking forward to seeing it again in 1986.

Comets were not always looked forward to with pleasure. Like eclipses, they seemed to be accidents in the midst of orderly, planetary traffic. To the ignorant and superstitious, comets were evil omens, foretelling death, plague, or war. There was always a war somewhere in the world, even if only a little war, that could be blamed on a newly arrived comet. As with eclipses, now that we know what comets are and can predict their motions, they are no longer feared.

Mark Twain, the great American writer and humorist, poked fun at the foolish notions people still held about comets as late as the beginning of this century. When he was already old, he said that he had a special affection for Halley's comet. He was born in 1835, the year of the comet. He

80

74. Giacobini's Comet, 1906. *On December 29, left, tail was relatively straight and narrow. On December 30, right, tail had become fan-shaped, broadening into a diffuse spray.*

expected to die when it came around next, he said. He did, indeed, die in 1910.

What Comets Look Like

A comet is usually made up of three parts: a brilliant nucleus, which may be only a few miles wide or as large as the earth; a head, called the coma, in the form of a bright cloud up to 100,000 miles in diameter surrounding the nucleus; and a glowing tail which resembles a veil of very thin gas trailing out for up to 100 million miles. Some comets, however, appear headless and tailless, retaining only the nucleus as a hazy globe of light. Other comets contain more than one nucleus. Still others have been observed to have several tails (the comet of 1744 having no fewer than six).

A respected theory holds that the nucleus is composed of rocky fragments packed together with water, methane, and ammonia, which must exist as ice particles because of the very low temperatures of interplanetary space. The head and tail, on the other hand, contain so little material that stars in the background can easily be seen through them. The earth could collide with a comet's tail without damage. In fact, no one would notice the collision. It would be like a bullet passing through a spider's web.

75. Comet Cunningham, December 21, 1940. *Motion of the comet was along the white streaks left by stars as the camera was moved to keep the comet in focus. The tail of the comet streams out in an entirely different direction, away from the sun, under the pressure of the sun's radiation.*

Chemicals in comets are revealed by spectroscopic examination of the light from the head and tail. This light appears to be due partly to reflected sunlight and partly to a glow that occurs after particles absorb sunlight.

The head and tail seem to be sprayed forcefully out of the solid nucleus like steam from an overheated boiler. Several theories have been suggested to explain why this happens, but the cause is still not completely understood. There is a common mistake made about the direction of a comet's tail. It does not stream out behind the comet like a scarf on a runner's neck. Instead, it tends to point always away from the sun. The forces acting on the particles in the tail are the attraction toward the sun by the sun's gravitation and a repulsion away from the sun by the pressure of the sun's rays. The pressure of the rays is greater than the gravitational attraction. This causes the tail to drift away from the sun as if on a solar breeze, regardless of the direction of motion of the comet.

The tail does not always point away from the sun. Sometimes, when there is more than one tail, the tails fan out like fingers. It is possible that other forces, not yet taken into account, are also acting on the tail of a comet. The behavior of the tail is just one mystery connected with comets.

When a comet ejects its tail, it probably loses all control over it. The head is too small and light in weight to exert much pull by gravitation. Therefore, comets are forever scattering portions of their tails in their wake as they race across the skies.

76. Meteor shower. *On the evening of November 27, 1872, the fragments remaining from the breaking up of Biela's Comet passed through the earth's atmosphere. Friction caused the fragments to heat up and glow in a spectacular shower of shooting stars.*

Tails have been seen to become detached from the heads. Each time Halley's comet approaches the sun, it dons a new tail for the occasion.

The Adventurous Life of Biela's Comet   In 1827 M. Gambart, a French astronomer, was studying the motion of a small comet, discovered only a few days earlier by another astronomer named Wilhelm von Biela. Just as Halley had done for the first time in history over a hundred years before, Gambart noticed that the path of this new comet was like that of two previous comets. These had been observed in 1772 and 1805. Gambart calculated the period to be approximately six and three-quarter years. Some of the visits of this comet had either not been noticed, or its position at those times had not been favorable for viewing. Now that it was proved to be a periodic comet, it was named after its discoverer, Biela.

There was a public scare when it was announced that the orbit of Biela's comet intersected the earth. A devastating collision was feared. However, the inhabitants of the earth were assured that a collision with the comet, if it occurred, would not be felt in any way.

Biela's comet returned punctually in 1832. It is assumed that it came back also in 1839, but its position was again unfavorable and it was not seen. In the winter of 1845-46, astronomers made the astonishing discovery that the comet had split in two. Two comets were observed, each complete with head, nucleus, and tail, traveling together like celestial sisters. They reappeared in September, 1852. This time they were farther apart than when last seen in 1846.

The comet, or comets, were not missed when they did not appear in 1859. Their position in the sky was expected to interfere with observations. However, they should have been visible in 1866, but could not be found. When they were not seen in 1872, they were assumed lost. Comets with short periods tend to come too close to the sun. The severe forces of the sun may break the comet into fragments. Therefore, short periods sometimes mean short lives.

However, about seven o'clock in the evening, on November 27, 1872, the earth was literally bombarded with a shower of "falling stars." They were described as falling like snow. The sky was crisscrossed with bright streaks. It was roughly estimated that some 160,000 "falling stars" must have flashed across the sky that night. The display, which lasted five hours, is pictured in figure 76.

This sudden eruption of heavenly fireworks broke out just twelve weeks after the time Biela's comet had been expected to arrive. What had apparently happened was that Biela's comet had come too close either to the sun or to the giant planet, Jupiter. The gravitational force of the huge, nearby body had scattered the lumps of matter that make up the interior of the head of the comet. First the comet was broken into two, the pair of comets that were seen in 1846. The next time the two comets must have been torn apart into far-flung bits. As a result, they were never again seen as comets. However, the scattered fragments continued to travel along roughly the same path as the original comet. On the night of November 27, this cloud of particles, which had once been a comet, must have enveloped the earth. The collision of these fragments with the earth's atmosphere caused the spectacular demonstration of "falling stars."

77. Meteor. *A very bright meteor left this trail across a photograph of the constellations Perseus, Andromeda, and parts of Taurus. Meteors may be fragments of a broken planet still in orbit through our solar system, revealing themselves when they collide with our atmosphere.*

84

Meteors and Meteorites Although the star-fall of November 27, 1872 was extraordinary, individual "falling stars," or "shooting stars," are a common experience. As you watch the night sky, a star seems to detach itself from the black background. It sweeps silently across part of the sky, seeming to leave a luminous trail, and then vanishes. Sometimes it is over so quickly, you are not sure it happened at all.

A star does not really *fall*. A fast flying fragment from space penetrates our atmosphere. Just as a rope pulled swiftly through our hands can heat our skin, friction with the particles of air heats the fragment of matter. The fragment, called a *meteor,* is traveling so fast that it is heated to incandescence. If it is small, it is completely consumed by burning before it reaches the ground. If it is large enough, some remains may fall to the earth.

Every day about one billion of these meteors enter the earth's atmosphere. On the average, however, only one of this vast number succeeds in touching the ground. The rest become dispersed as a gas throughout the atmosphere. Since so few of these meteors actually fall to earth, we are in little danger of being struck by one. Moreover, two-thirds of the earth is covered by water. The few particles that do reach the surface of the earth are more likely to splash into the ocean than anywhere else. The remains of meteors that do survive their searing voyage through the air are called *meteorites.*

Meteorites of all sizes have been found, from microscopic grains of dust to huge boulders weighing several tons. Collections of tiny, spherical meteorites have been taken from the bottoms of oceans and the tops of high mountains. These are little balls because they are formed from molten droplets cast off by the hot meteorite body during its passage through the air. The droplets cool and harden before they land on the earth. Compare these meteorite beads with the 60-ton rock that fell near Grootfontein in South Africa. This rock, given the name Hoba, is almost 10 feet across and 4 feet thick. In various parts of the world, great circular depressions in the earth have been seen from airplanes. Some of these are filled with water to form lakes. It is now believed that these may be signs of the impacts of tremendous meteorites.

Where does all this meteoric material come from? It appears that there are streams of small, solid bodies flowing through our planetary system, traveling about the sun in elliptical orbits like so many tiny comets. Periodically, these streams come near the earth and large quantities of the small bodies cross through our atmosphere. Others may be diverted by the gravitational pull of the earth so that they are drawn off course into our atmosphere. They become heated by collisions with the air particles and cause the showers of falling stars that are seen toward the end of summer and into the fall and winter months. Meteor showers commonly occur on August 10, October 20, November 14, and December 10.

The orbits of these streams of solid bodies seem to coincide with the orbits of certain comets. The full relationship between comets and meteor streams is not known, but it seems evident that they are related. It is possible that meteors are made of solid material thrown out by comets. They may also be the scattered remains of comets that were somehow destroyed, like Biela's comet. Recent work in astronomy shows some promise of coming closer to an answer to the riddle of the meteors.

Meteorites are divided into two classes by composition: *iron,* primarily iron and nickel with traces of other elements; and *stony,* containing various minerals with bits of iron. As the only objects we have from outside our own planet, meteorites are fascinating clues to the composition of interplanetary bodies.

The solar family is now complete. However far the members roam, their motions are influenced chiefly by the sun, in accordance with the Law of Universal Gravitation — obeyed no less by the giant Jupiter than by the most minute meteor.

78. Meteorite, Canyon Diablo Crater, Arizona. *Meteors are mostly particles which glow with frictional heat as they enter our atmosphere. Some are chunks of stone or metal large enough to survive until they reach the ground where they are called meteorites. Ranging from grains of dust to boulders of many tons which dig craters when they strike, meteorites have a glassy outer skin formed from their previously molten surface. This meteorite measures 5 inches in length.*

Our Visible Universe

THE SOLAR SYSTEM contains a large number of objects—the sun, the planets, their satellites, the planetoids, comets, meteors —but most of these are not even visible except through a telescope. Those that can be seen on a clear night do not account for more than a few specks out of the great multitude of stars that fill the sky. What do we know of these other stars? The planets are only our nearest neighbors in space. What lies beyond them and our solar system?

We have already peered into space as far as Pluto, almost four billion miles. In our imagination, we have even traveled beyond Pluto as we followed a non-periodic comet to the outer tip of its orbit. Before we go any farther, let us pause and simply scan the starry sky the way men have done since the most ancient times.

The Constellations What we see in the night sky are millions of scattered spots of light, like so many shiny nailheads stuck in a huge, black ceiling. Like our ancestors, we are attracted first to the brighter ones.

These bright stars are not spread across the sky in a perfectly uniform fashion but, rather, are grouped in clusters of varied shapes.

Clusters, or star-groups, are called *constellations*. A constellation is not always a well-defined group. It is simply a number of stars that either seem closer to each other than to other stars, or seem to form some recognizable shape. Some constellations have outlying stars that might just as well be assigned to another constellation. They are not much closer to one than to the other. Sometimes two constellations may be near enough to each other so that there is doubt whether they should be considered as two separate groups. They might also be taken together as one larger constellation.

Because it is sometimes a matter of opinion how best to group the stars, the number of constellations had to be fixed by general agreement among astronomers. In the United States we abide by the decision of a committee of the International Astronomical Union. We group the stars into

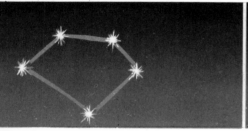

80. Constellations 100,000 years from now. *The stars in constellations are moving in different directions at different speeds. They move fast, but the distances are so vast that the constellations appear to change shape very slowly. Upper row shows familiar constellations of Cassiopeia, Ursa Major, and Ursa Minor as they appear now. Lower row shows how they may look in about 100,000 years.*

88 constellations. In Italy, on the other hand, the Italian Association of Astronomers has lumped the three constellations, Vela, Puppis, and Carina into one great constellation called Argo. Thus, in Italy there are considered to be only 86 constellations.

Earlier stargazers also divided the sky in another way, to make it easier to describe. It is a fact that the ellipses along which the planets move all lie almost in the same plane. This means that our solar system is similar to a group of large balls rolling about on a single, flat table top. Even the planetoids tend to skid around on this same, flat plane. If we imagine that this plane is a thick, round disk with a diameter as big as we please, then it also stretches out to the distant stars. It is now a huge, round, flat box that contains the sun,

the planets, the asteroids, and any stars that lie between the top and the bottom of the box. This region is called the *Zodiac*.

Of the 88 constellations, 12 lie within the Zodiac, 28 lie north of or above it, and 48 lie south of or below it. The purpose of inventing ideas like the Zodiac and the constellations is to provide a convenient means for mapping the stars. They enable us to define the positions of the stars as they appear to us on earth.

To the spirited imagination of the ancient stargazers, the varied forms of the constellations sometimes suggested the shapes of animals, or people, or common objects. The names that have come down to us from those times reflect these associations. There are Apus the bird of paradise, Aquila the eagle, Aries the ram, Camelopardus the giraffe, Cetus the whale,

90

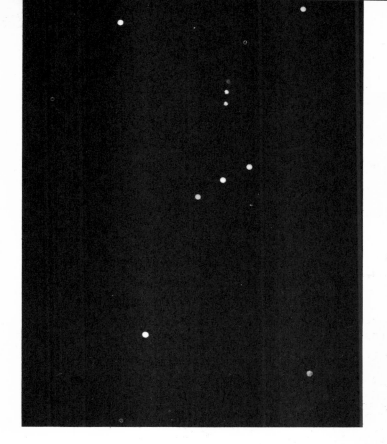

81. Part of constellation Orion. *About 10 of the brightest stars in Orion are made larger by adjusting the telescope slightly out of focus. Orion was a mythological Greek hunter. The four corner stars outline his figure. The three stars in a diagonal line are his belt from which hangs his knife, three stars in an almost vertical line.*

Draco the dragon, Leo the lion, Pisces the fishes, Sagitta the arrow and Sagittarius the archer, Ursa Major the great bear and Ursa Minor the little bear, and Vulpecula the little fox. Then there are the water bearer, the dogs, the crab, the lady in a chair, Berenice's hair, the furnace, the clock, the microscope, the painter's easel, the mariner's compass, the telescope, the triangle, and even the air pump. When they ran out of animals and objects, these ancestors of ours named the constellations after heroes like Hercules and Perseus. Some are shown in figures 83 and 84.

It was once thought that the names and legends of the constellations started in ancient Greece, almost a thousand years before Christ. However, writings have been found on clay tablets much older than the Greek civilization, indicating that descriptions of the constellations existed long before. It seems probable that the Greeks had inherited a large part of the names and stories connected with the constellations

82. Nebula in Orion. *A bright patch under the three-star belt of Orion, after long film exposure, blossoms into a striking picture of two gaseous nebulae. The Great Nebula and the Small Nebula, M42 and M43 (numbers in Messier's catalogue), are part of a larger nebula that covers much of Orion. It is a cloud of thin gas, mostly hydrogen, swirling rapidly in space about 1000 light years away from earth.*

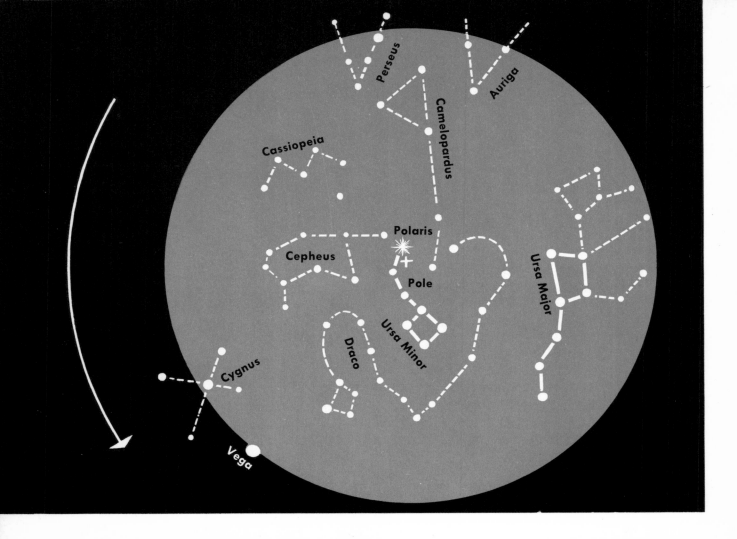

83. Stars and constellations near Polaris (North Star). *Constellations are artificial groupings of stars for convenience of identification. One star in a constellation may be more distant than another,* *but we look toward the same part of the sky to see both. The Pole is a point directly above the earth's North Pole. Arrow shows direction in which stars circle overhead due to rotation of the earth.*

from earlier peoples like the Sumerians and Accadians. Groups of stars may have been recognized earlier than 3000 B.C.

Now let us go back to the question of what we know about the stars. The stars are not fixed spots on a black ceiling as they appear, nor are they grouped into fancifully shaped constellations. The constellations are really an optical illusion.

When we say that two stars seem close together, all we mean is that we do not have to turn our eyes very much to look from one to the other. Since one star may be very

far behind the other, their actual separation in space may be great. The comparison between the real distance and the apparent distance between stars is pictured in figure 85.

The real significance of a constellation, then, is that it defines a direction in which to look to find a star. It does not mean that the stars in that constellation are close to each other or that they are related to each other in any way.

This raises a new question. If the stars are not arranged conveniently in simple clusters, are they organized in any way at all? Or are they merely distributed at random throughout infinite space? As you will soon see, there is organization in the heavens.

The Galaxy Galileo, with his telescope, was the great explorer of our solar system. Our sun has proved to be but one star in an enormous group of stars, among which there may be many more solar systems like ours. This large group is called the *Galaxy*. What Galileo did for our sun and planets, Sir William and Sir John Herschel, father and son, did for the Galaxy.

Evidence for the existence of the Galaxy lies in the appearance of the Milky Way. In fact, the name Galaxy comes from the Greek word for milk. The Milky Way is a hazy, white ribbon of stars that arches over-head from horizon to horizon. We see it best when the night is cloudless and moon-less. On such a night the sky seems literally spattered with stars. If we look carefully, however, we see that they are relatively widely dispersed in most places. But in the region of the Milky Way, the stars appear to be so densely concentrated that they blend into a luminous stripe, like a brush

84. Constellation Ursa Minor. *The unknown ancient stargazer who named this constellation imagined that it had the outline of a Little Bear (translation from the Latin). The tip of the tail is the North Star, Polaris. The shape of the seven-star figure also suggested its other name, Little Dipper.*

85. Real and Apparent Distance Between Stars. *Star ¹ is a great distance from Star ², but from earth they appear to be side by side and closer together.*

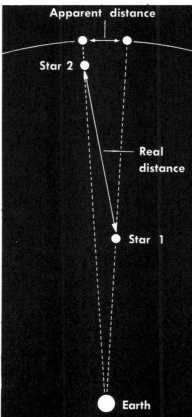

86. Our Galaxy. *Except for its spiral arms, our Galaxy might appear to an outsider as a flattened disk with a bulging center. The long arrow marks the position of our sun and solar system. When, from earth, we sight in any direction along the plane of the disk, we peer into the thick of the stars. They appear as the Milky Way, a dense band of stars across the night sky. In other directions, we are looking up out of the disk and see only the relatively few stars between us and surrounding space.*

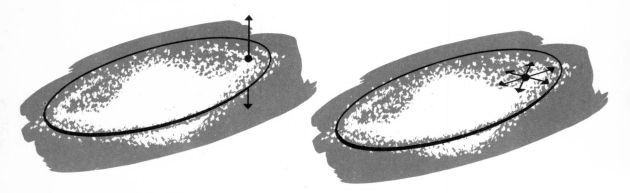

stroke across the sky. If we could walk over the earth rapidly enough to follow the night around the globe, we would find that the arc of the Milky Way does not end at the horizons. It continues until it closes into a complete circle, dividing the sky into two halves.

The explanation of this is that the Galaxy has the shape of a large, flat disk with a bulge at the middle, as illustrated in figures 86 and 87. Imagine that the outer edge of this disk is a circle drawn on a sheet of paper. The line in the picture drawn from one end of the Galaxy to the other is the edge of the paper. We are standing near

the sun, whose position is mar[k] arrow. If we look along the p[l] Galaxy—that is, along the surf imaginary paper—we see the M We are looking directly into the of stars, and they seem closely we look toward the central bu Galaxy, the stars will be especia ous. If we look toward the e[d] Galaxy just to the right of the picture, the stars will seem fewe quite dense.

If, instead, we look at right an plane—that is, up or down from nary sheet of paper—we ar

94

87. Spiral nebula in Virgo. *This nebula, called M104 or NGC (New General Catalogue) 4594, is a spiral galaxy similar to our own seen edge on. The rim looks dark because of its high dust content which absorbs light. At the center, the bulging halo is composed of many stars blurred together.*

through the thickness of the Galaxy. Since the thickness of the galactic disk is very thin compared with the diameter, we now see a much smaller number of stars.

Now that we have discovered the shape of the Galaxy, the unequal distribution of stars in the sky is understandable. The Herschels did not have this advantage a century and a half ago. We have arrived at our present understanding only because of their systematic exploration of the stars and because of later scientific studies inspired by their findings.

Now we must change our picture of the Galaxy a little. It was found that the outer edge of the Galaxy is not a round circle. There are two offshoots that flare out like streamers on the rim of a turning wheel. The true appearance of the Galaxy is that of a giant spiral. There is a central nucleus, which we earlier called a bulge, from which two spiral arms seem to be unwinding. The image of the disk with a bulging center is not too inaccurate, however, and was used

to simplify the explanation of the Milky Way. A picture of another spiral cluster of stars may be seen in figures 90 and 91.

The Galaxy constitutes most of our visible universe. It contains our solar system and almost all the stars we see in the sky, with rare exceptions. We will come to these rare exceptions later. We can see the planets in our solar system only because they reflect light from the sun. They are not hot enough to emit their own light directly. The fact that we can see so many distant stars, far beyond our solar system, means that there must be many other hot, glowing stars like our sun. These are too far to be seen by reflected light alone. Indeed, there are many suns in our Galaxy, some as big as ours, many more that are bigger, and a few that are smaller. Some of these stars are very bright, some moderately bright, and some are dim. We assume that some of these probably have planets

and a solar system similar to our own. We cannot see these planets because, if they are anything like our own, they are too small, too dark, and too close to their suns for us to distinguish them at such great distances.

The Light Year and the Size of the Galaxy

How great are these distances? Pluto seemed far enough away, at almost four billion miles, to satisfy anyone's appetite for large distances. The answer is that the size of the Galaxy is so much greater than anything we have met previously, we must invent a new way to describe it.

When we deal with very small dimensions, we use inches, or fractions of an inch. If the distances are larger, we find it convenient to use feet, each foot representing 12 inches. When the distances grow still bigger, as the lengths of roads between cities, we measure them in miles. Each mile

88. Mosaic of the Milky Way. *A series of pictures connected end to end portrays the Milky Way as it sweeps across the sky from Sagittarius toward the south to Cassiopeia toward the north. It is equivalent to viewing our Galaxy edge on from the inside.*

89. Carina Arm of our Galaxy. *A number of spiral arms of our Galaxy have been distinguished and named, generally after the constellation toward which they lie. Looking toward the Carina Arm, we see a number of details revealed by a new telescope, including small dark globules. These hazy blobs are dust concentrations in which it is believed new stars are being born.*

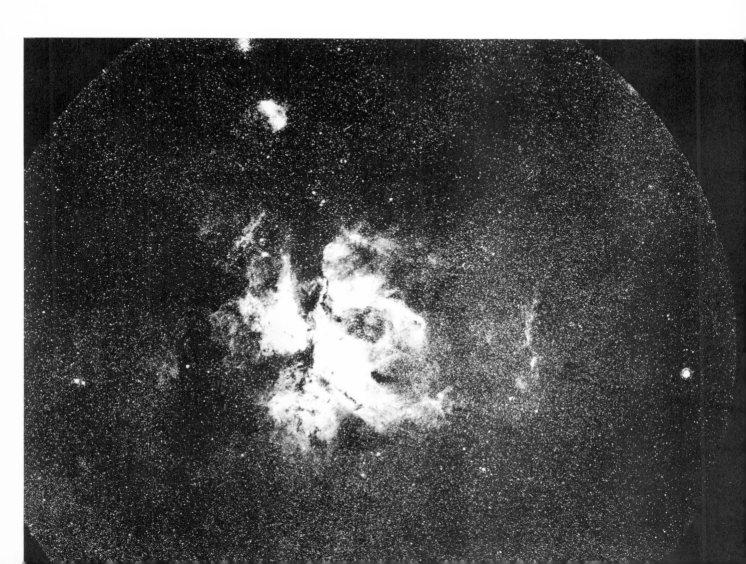

is 5280 feet. Every time we write down a distance of one mile, we save ourselves the trouble of writing 5280 feet, or 63,360 inches.

Within our own solar system, the distances are so large that we had to use miles to describe them. Even then, the number of miles had risen to figures with nine zeros. When we now turn to a study of the Galaxy, the number of zeros becomes hopelessly awkward to write down. Instead we turn to a new unit of distance, the *light year*.

In spite of its name, the light year is not a unit of time. It is a distance, just like inches, feet, and miles. It is the distance light travels in a year.

It may come as a surprise that light has a speed of travel. When we see an electric light go on, it seems to us that the light reaches our eyes immediately. This is not true. The time is extremely short, but it does have a finite value. The reason the time is so short is that light travels 186,000 miles in one second. Since there are 60 seconds in a minute, light covers a distance of $60 \times 186,000$ or 11,160,000 miles every minute. With 60 minutes to an hour, light travels about 670,000,000 miles an hour. There are 24 hours in a day, so light completes a trip of over 16,000,000,000 miles a day. Finally, with 365 days to the year, we can calculate the distance light travels in a year—that is, one light year. This is a distance of approximately 5,880,000,-000,000 miles. Compare this with the mere 93,000,000 miles between the earth and sun.

Now we can give the dimensions of the Galaxy. Referring again to figure 86, the distance from one edge of the Galaxy to

90. Double galaxy in Canes Venatici. *The large spiral, NGC 5194, is joined to the small one, NGC 5195, by an extended spiral arm. Many such multiple galaxies have been discovered. It is likely that the galaxies have a tidal effect on each other which influences the shape of the arms.*

OPPOSITE:

91. Andromeda nebula. *This flat twirling spiral of stars in the constellation of Andromeda is a galaxy very much like our own but considerably larger. It is over 2 million light years away. This nebula serves as a model from which we can learn characteristics of our own Galaxy otherwise inaccessible.*

the diametrically opposed edge is about 100,000 light years. The thickness at the center is over 15,000 light years, dwindling down to an average of 4000 light years in the outer portions. Our sun lies in one of the spiral arms, about 30,000 light years from the center.

We asked before, what lies beyond our solar system? Beyond our solar system lie all the stars in the Galaxy. If we were able to ride on a light beam out past Pluto until we came to the nearest star in the Galaxy, our closest neighbor, the trip would require 4 years. This is another way of saying that this star is 4 light years away. Likewise, it takes 4 years for light from this star to reach us.

Even light from the sun, which is so much closer to us, requires a little over 8 minutes to reach us. When we see a flare erupt from the surface of the sun, we really see it as it was 8 minutes ago.

It is almost impossible for our minds to grasp the immensity of the Galaxy. The leap from miles to light years is almost too much for our earth-bound imaginations to accomplish.

The Number of Stars in the Galaxy   In all this immensity of galactic space, how many stars are there? Well, during a clear, dark night, a man with good vision can count slightly more than 2000 stars. With the help of a small telescope, he can raise this number to more than one million. Through a large telescope he can see perhaps 100 million stars. If he is permitted to use the largest telescope in the world, and he takes

photographs to save time and eyesight, he can locate over 500 million stars. The largest telescope in the world is the one at Mount Palomar Observatory in California. It has a reflecting mirror 200 inches in diameter and makes the moon appear to be only 19 miles away.

Since we cannot possibly see all the stars in the Galaxy, the true total number must be much greater than 500 million. Estimates of this total number made by different astronomers have yielded different results. Considering the complexity of the problem, this was to be expected. What is remarkable is the degree of agreement. Estimates have generally fallen between about 10 and 100 billion stars as the total population of our Galaxy.

If the astronomers cannot see the stars, how can they count them? The method they use is similar to the one used in an old, humorous story. A cowhand was famous for his ability to count a herd of cattle rush-

92. Mount Wilson Observatory. *On a mountain northeast of Los Angeles this observatory houses a 100-inch and a 60-inch telescope among other equipment. It is now handicapped by light from nearby cities. Mount Wilson shares a joint program with the more favorably placed Mount Palomar Observatory which operates the 200-inch Hale telescope, the largest optical telescope in the world.*

93. Layout of the 200-inch Hale telescope. *One can clearly see the size and complexity of the large telescope, its supporting framework, and its controlling machinery. However, the bearings on which the structure rides are so free of friction that only a small motor is needed to drive the system.*

OPPOSITE:

94. Hale telescope in operation. *An observer sits in the cage located at the focal point of the curved 200-inch-diameter mirror gleaming below. The mirror weighs 14.5 tons. Over 5 tons of glass were removed in the grinding and polishing of the original 20-ton disk. From initial conception to first use, the Hale telescope required some 19 years of planning and construction.*

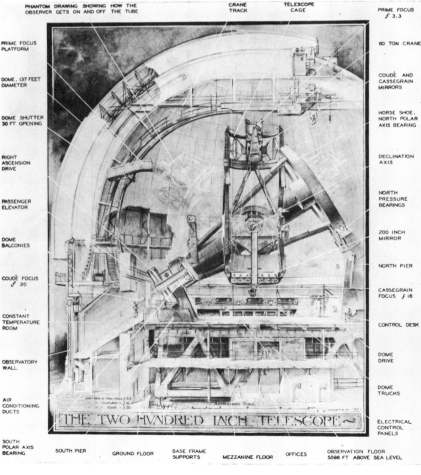

ing by him across the prairie. When asked his secret, he replied, "I count the legs and divide by four." The astronomer assumes that the average star has about the same weight as our sun. The weight of each star is like the number of legs on each steer. Then the astronomer figures the total weight of the Galaxy and divides by the average weight of a star. This gives him the number of stars.

He still must know the total weight of the Galaxy. To explain how the astronomer finds this, we must go back to Newton's Law of Universal Gravitation.

Every star in the Galaxy exerts a force of attraction on every other star. The forces are not all equal. Stars very far apart will have little effect on each other; stars closer together will feel each other's force more strongly. Large stars have greater influence than small stars. Despite all these complications, there are consequences of Newton's Law that simplify the situation. Let us use our sun to illustrate this.

The sun is 30,000 light years away from the center of the Galaxy. Draw an imaginary circle about the center, using 30,000 light years as a radius. This circle will cut all the stars at this distance from the center, including our sun. It will also enclose all the stars that are closer to the center than 30,000 light years. It can be shown that the total gravitational force on our sun depends only on the stars within the circle. The forces from those outside the circle completely cancel each other; for every star pulling one way, there is another pulling with equal force in the opposite direction.

It can also be shown that the stars within the circle act as if all their weight was concentrated in just one immense star at the center of the Galaxy.

So, instead of having to calculate all the forces separately, we need deal with only one force and one mass. (We have used mass and weight as if they were the same thing. They are not, but the difference will be explained later in the book. For the present, it is enough that both are related to heaviness.)

Just as our earth pursues its orbit about the sun, our sun rotates about the center of the Galaxy. The sun makes one complete revolution in 200 million years. From the knowledge of the mass of the sun and the shape and size of its orbit, a calculation can be made of the force causing the motion of the sun. This force, in turn, permits the calculation of the attracting mass of the stars within the imaginary circle.

Since we know how much of the Galaxy is contained within this circle, we can calculate what the mass of the total Galaxy must be. It must be taken into account that not all the matter in the Galaxy is compacted into stars. Some of it is dispersed in the form of enormous clouds of gas and dust, but it still exerts a gravitational force. Mak-

95. Birth of a star. *Although no one really knows the origin of stars, a respected theory holds that they congealed out of clouds of dust and gas. Through gravitational attraction for each other, particles became compressed, leading to high temperatures and the starting of nuclear reactions, the source of a star's heat and light. Little motions in the parent cloud gave rise to rotation of the hot globe about its axis.*

96. Jodrell Bank Radio Telescope. *Since it was discovered that some heavenly objects emit radio waves, giant receiving antennas have been built to collect radio waves from space. This mammoth saucer, located in Cheshire, England, weighs over 2000 tons, has a diameter of 250 feet, and yet can be steered precisely to follow a star. It can also transmit radar pulses and receive echoes reflected from celestial objects.*

97. Control room—Jodrell Bank Radio Telescope. *All motions of the giant telescope antenna are directed from the console at the center of the control room. Meters read and record coordinate angles and times of observations.*

ing a correction for this, and then dividing the remainder of the mass of the Galaxy by the mass of a single sun, we arrive at a number of 100 billion.

Thus, there are approximately 100 billion stars in the Galaxy with an average mass per star equal to that of our sun. There is evidence that the assumption is really accurate, that the average star in the Galaxy has about the same mass as our sun.

The sky is sometimes described as being composed of moving planets and fixed stars. We see that this is false. All the stars are really moving, their paths determined by the net gravitational force of all their companions in the Galaxy. The stars are called fixed because they seem to be standing still, appearing each night always at the same point. This illusion is caused by distance. A ship on the distant horizon may be cutting swiftly across the ocean. From the shore it seems to be moving very slowly, if at all. The so-called fixed stars are so far away that their motions are not apparent.

From the large number of these stars, it might be supposed that space is as crowded as Grand Central Station at rush hour, with just as much danger of collisions. Actually, the size of the Galaxy is so enormous, that exactly the reverse is the case. A human being in space, instead of being crushed by the throng, would feel utterly and distressingly alone. A star is a lonely voyager in an apparently endless void, with no chance of meeting another star in hundreds of thousands of billions of years.

Star Companions Not all stars are as completely alone as others. For instance, our sun is comforted by its family of planets and satellites, and we presume that some other stars have planetary systems as well. A primary characteristic of such a system is that the central body, or sun, is large in size, whereas the planets are relatively small.

Another kind of system is found frequently. It consists of two stars that travel together like inseparable companions. Since neither is much smaller than the other, they are not like planet and sun, but are two full-fledged stars. Such a pair is called a *binary system.* The two stars are bound to each other by mutual gravitational attraction. They orbit about the center of the Galaxy as a pair, also rotating about each other as they go.

98. Polar star trails. *A camera was pointed vertically upward at the North Pole, its line of sight parallel to the earth's axis, and its shutter was held open for 8 hours 2 minutes (approximately one third of a revolution of the earth). As the earth turned, the stars traced circular paths on the film, each completing one third of a circle.*

99. 600-foot radio telescope. *Near Sugar Grove, West Virginia, the U. S. Navy has built what is called the world's largest precision instrument. It is a parabolic dish antenna 600 feet in diameter, completely maneuverable in spite of its 2-million-pound aluminum body. Unlike optical telescopes, it can operate day and night, rain or shine.*

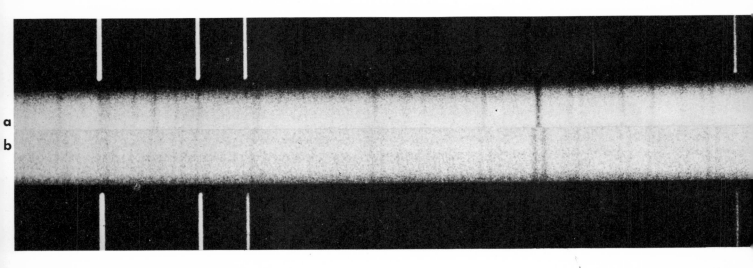

a
b

100. Spectroscope detects double star. *Hazy lines denote wave lengths of light from two stars so close together they appear as one. The stars are twirling in space like the ends of a baton; as one swings toward the earth, the other swings away. Just as a horn sound rises in pitch as a car approaches and* *falls as it speeds away, so the wave lengths of starlight shift up or down with the motion of a star. This is called the Doppler Effect. The presence of two stars is revealed because their opposite motions split single lines in spectrum a into double lines in spectrum b.*

The Restless Galaxy   There is nothing so peaceful as to lie on one's back on a warm, dark night, soothed by the stillness of the stars in the sky. Except for the occasional meteor, the universe seems suspended and motionless.

While we lie there peacefully, the earth is spinning like a top, swirling about the sun simultaneously. The moon revolves about the earth, pirouetting all the while. All the other planets join in the merry dance. While the planets whirl, the sun pulls them along in a wide sweep. as the Galaxy turns upon itself. The wheeling motions do not stop there. The Galaxy itself, as one great mass, full of internal twistings and turnings, is racing through space away from neighboring galaxies, leaving them farther behind at a rate of between 750 and 38,000 miles per second.

To us, lying tranquil on the soft grass, this mad rush of stars through space is less immediate than the brush of a gentle breeze across our face.

The Variety of the Stars   We said before that these racing stars have something in common. They almost all have approximately the same mass as our own sun. However, they do vary in other respects, such as color, dimensions, and brightness.

The mass of the sun, about 330,000 times that of the earth, is 2 billion billion billion tons. This is the number 2 followed by 27 zeros. Each ton is equal to 2000 pounds. The mass in pounds would be the

106

number 4 followed by 30 zeros. To show how impressive this number really is, we will write it out as follows:

4,000,000,000,000,000,000,000,000,000,000

pounds

When there are so many zeros, it is easy to write down the wrong number. Perhaps it would not even be noticeable if there were one zero more or less. As Sir Arthur Eddington, the late British astronomer, remarked, we might not notice it, but Nature would. In the entire Galaxy, it is rare for a star to have a mass more than ten times the above number, or less than one-tenth of it. Such stars would be exceptionally heavy or exceptionally light.

Although there is such remarkable uniformity in the masses of the stars, this uniformity does not apply to their actual sizes. There are many very large stars, but in these matter is packed loosely and the density is low. In the very small stars, the matter is highly compressed and the density is correspondingly great.

An example of an extremely large star is Antares in the constellation Scorpio. It fills a space 90 million times greater than the size of our sun, but contains only a slightly larger quantity of matter. It is about 30 times heavier than the sun. The sun is therefore 3 million times denser than Antares. The interior of Antares is consequently not a solid body, but is more like a spray of fine powder.

At the opposite extreme is one of the smallest stars known, the star of Van Maanen. This star is even smaller than the earth. Two and one-half million stars of this size could fit into the sun and still rattle around like marbles in a fishbowl. Although the sun has a volume almost 3 million times that of the star of Van Maanen, the mass of the sun is only about 7 times as great. This means that the density of the star of Van Maanen is about 400,000 times greater than that of the sun. A piece of matter the size of a cherry cut from this dwarf star would weigh approximately one ton.

Even with the naked eye, it can be seen that stars vary also in color. Some stars seem brilliant white, other are more reddish or yellowish. Through a telescope fitted to a spectroscope, these colors can be analyzed. We saw earlier how the colors in the light from the sun provided information about the temperature and composition of the surface of the sun. Here, the same relationship holds. The colors of the stars, as seen in the spectroscope, are clues to how hot the stars are and of what they are composed.

A wide range of temperatures is found. The colder stars have surface temperatures as low as 3000°F, as compared with the 11,000°F of the sun. The hottest stars have surface temperatures ranging over 100,000°F.

Brightness and temperature are also related, hotter stars tending to be brighter. Their appearance to us on earth, however, may be misleading because the stars are at different distances from us. A bright star far away may appear dim. A relatively cool

star may seem unusually bright because it is closer to us.

Thus, although the stars are all made of the same materials in almost the same amounts, they exhibit a marvelous variety. The most brilliant star is a million million times brighter than the faintest. The diameter of the largest stars may be 300,000 times that of the smallest. One star is billions of times denser than another. Some stars have low densities at the surface, the density increasing as the center is approached. With other stars, this does not happen at all. Temperatures are found to vary by hundreds of thousands of degrees.

If star collecting were a hobby like stamp collecting, the hobbyist would enjoy a magnificent diversity of specimens.

The Life of the Stars Although the differences among stars are very large, the number of varieties is not infinite. Like man, stars are born, live out their lives, and die, each age putting its stamp upon a star's features. A deep red color signifies a relatively low star temperature. This is associated with birth or young age, when a star is beginning to warm up, and with old age, when a star is already failing. The dimensions and color of a star are both related to the stage reached by the star in its life cycle. Just as we would not expect to find an old

101. Nova Puppis. *A new star (nova) in the constellation Puppis suddenly brightened to thousands of times its former intensity and then faded. A nova is a star that explodes for incompletely known reasons, often leaving behind a nebula after it returns to its earlier condition.*

man with the smooth skin of a baby, or a two-year-old who is 6 feet tall, there are combinations of characteristics which are not found among stars. For example, there are huge red stars and dwarf red stars, but there are no red stars of intermediate size. The reason will be found in the way a star is born, how it develops, and how it gradually fades.

Consider the probable history of our sun and our predictions of its future. It all began a long, long time ago.

In the midst of an enormous expanse of dust and gas, the particles in one region begin to condense. It is not clear what local disturbance causes the particles to come closer together in this particular region. This partial concentration, still of very low density, is called a *proto-star,* or the forerunner of a star. The contraction continues, helped by the gravitational attraction among the particles, which increases as they come closer to each other. As the particles compact into a greater density, pressures increase, temperatures rise, and the proto-star becomes brighter. A star is born (figure 95). Eventually the pressure, density, and temperature at the center are great enough to start the nuclear reaction which converts hydrogen into helium with a tremendous release of energy. The tendency of the ball of hot matter to compress further is counterbalanced by the internal pressures and the contraction stops. For our sun, this point was reached after about 25 million years.

An equilibrium is now established, which continues for a long time. The nu-clear furnace converts hydrogen into helium at a rate of about one per cent of the total mass of the star every billion years. This is the stable, middle age in which our sun rests today. As long as the intense heat at the center does not cause too much turbulence, the star leads a quiet middle life. Conversion of hydrogen into helium will be restricted to the center of the star only, the hottest part. This region, therefore, has a composition that is different from the rest of the body of the star and is given a special name, the *nucleus.*

Since one particle of helium is formed from four of hydrogen, the helium is four times as heavy. The nuclear reaction thus concentrates a large volume of hydrogen into a smaller volume of heavier helium at the center of the star. In this way the nucleus of the star is continually collecting more and more of the total mass of the star. When our sun is about 9 billion years old (it is approximately half that age now), about ten per cent of its entire mass will be contained in the nucleus. It will then enter an age of violent activity, in contrast with its relatively peaceful existence up to that time.

The nucleus will begin to contract, raising temperatures and pressures to tremendous heights, while the outside shell of the sun will expand and cool. During the first part of this process, the star will grow redder and brighter and become a gigantic red star. During the last phase, however, the star will become unbalanced and the outer shell will be scattered into space, either gradually or abruptly in a kind of ex-

plosion. Only the bare nucleus will remain. This phase of violence will last about 5 to 10 billion years.

The nucleus will look like a bright white dwarf among stars. There are many such white dwarfs in the Galaxy. They are stars which have lost most of their hydrogen and must depend on less energetic fuels for their nuclear furnaces. Having contracted to extremely high densities, the tightly pressed matter in the star resists further contraction. In some billions of years, its activity dwindling, its source of energy diminishing, the dwarf star cools and fades from white to red to final extinction. At this stage our sun will have died.

Not every star passes through exactly these same stages of evolution. The story of a particular star will depend on the mass of the star, its speed of rotation about its own axis, local magnetism, and on the matter available to the star in the cloud of gas within which it is formed.

Our sun was born some 5 billion years ago. It still has about half of its middle age, 5 billion years of violence, and a final period of dwarf status ahead. It will die in about 10 billion years.

Before the sun dies, during the period of expansion of the outer shell, the sun will swell to 200 or 300 times its present size. It will be big enough and hot enough to raise the temperature on the earth to the boiling point of water, ending life as we know it. The sun will be so big, it will overtake and swallow its closer planetary children, Mercury, Venus, and perhaps even Earth.

Not too long ago, astronomers thought the sun was a tired star, doomed to early extinction. Now, thanks to the findings of nuclear physics, the sun is considered to be in the prime of life with a long future ahead.

Beyond the Galaxy   We have studied our Galaxy from our vantage point here on earth and have seen it as the Milky Way. We have imagined ourselves as hovering in space outside the Galaxy, looking inward. We saw a giant, flat spiral with a bulging middle. Now let us direct our gaze outward, away from the Galaxy. What lies beyond? Is there only an infinite void with perpetual darkness? The answer is no. We must recall that the Galaxy was stated to contain all the stars visible in our sky with some exceptions. These exceptions are stars that actually shine from outside the Galaxy.

Our Galaxy is an island universe in space, a tremendous cluster of stars full of internal churning motion. These whirling stars are prevented from scattering into space by mutual gravitational attraction, which permits them some freedom of motion but keeps them huddled together in the shape we call our Galaxy.

What are those stars like, that gleam dimly outside our Galaxy? This is the subject of our next discussion.

102. Extended nebula in the Pleiades star group. *The Pleiades nebula is an example of a reflection nebula which contains dust illuminated by the light from nearby stars. The light gives a continuous spectrum when viewed through a spectroscope.*

111

The Galaxies

WHEN GALILEO first viewed the satellites of Jupiter through his telescope, he found the ideal model for the shape of the entire solar system. Here was a large body about which smaller bodies revolved. We can never see all of the solar system at one time because we are part of it and can view it only from the inside. With Jupiter as a model, however, we can imagine the planetary arrangement. We can then check our observations of the individual planets against such a model to see if they are consistent with each other. Since they are consistent, we assume that our guess was a good one. We feel that we know how the solar system works!

After a long, laborious examination of the positions of stars and their motions through space, astronomers were able to imagine the shape of the Galaxy. This was truly a giant step in man's extension of his knowledge of the universe. It required a bold intelligence to suggest a wheel-like system of stars of such enormous magnitude, in which our earth and our sun are only insignificant pinpoints. It would be reassur-

ing if we could actually see the shape of our Galaxy by viewing it from a distance, the way we can see the contours of the earth from an airplane. This is not a far-fetched hope. Although we cannot venture outside our own Galaxy, it has been found that other such galaxies exist, and are visible to us.

Here and there in the sky there are little white spots, some of which appear to have irregular outlines. They look like tiny luminous clouds. Only four can be seen with the naked eye, but others are discernible through powerful telescopes. Two of these four most prominent cloudlets are really enormous systems of galaxies called the

103. Typical nebulae. *Nebula is Latin for mist or cloud. Early astronomers saw hazy patches in the sky, distinguishable from single stars, and called them all nebulae. Modern telescopes disclose that nebulae are many different things, such as other galaxies, star clusters, shells of gas around stars, or bright clouds of gas and dust in our own Galaxy. Nebulae may be numbered according to their listing in catalogues, such as that by Messier or the New General Catalogue, abbreviated NGC.*

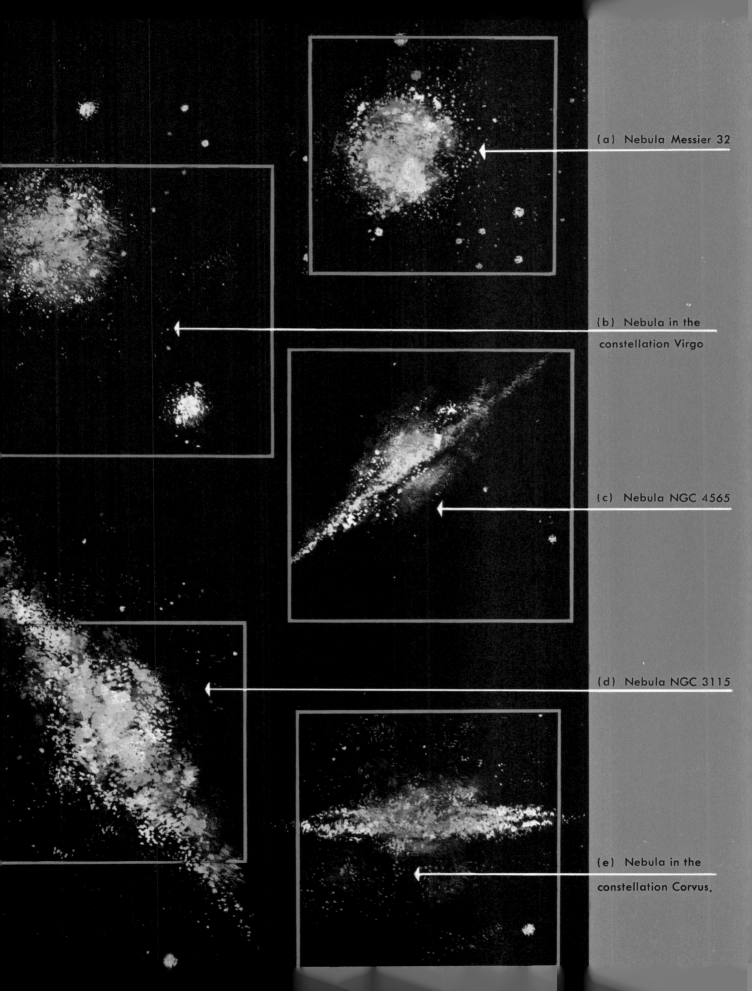

(a) Nebula Messier 32

(b) Nebula in the constellation Virgo

(c) Nebula NGC 4565

(d) Nebula NGC 3115

(e) Nebula in the constellation Corvus.

Clouds of Magellan. The other two are the nebula of Andromeda and the nebula of the Triangle. *Nebula* is the Latin word for mist. These are the exceptions that were mentioned before, the white spots in our night sky which do not belong to our Galaxy.

If we look more closely at the foremost of these nebulae, the nebula of Andromeda, we see not one hazy star, but a thick cluster of stars as shown in figure 91. Furthermore, these stars are distributed in the shape of a flattened disk with the character of a spiral swirl.

The spiral nebula of Andromeda is direct evidence of the existence of a galaxy with the shape we imagine possessed by our own. We can better visualize our solar system be-

cause we can see Jupiter and its twelve moons. We have a clearer picture of our Galaxy because we have photographs of the nebula of Andromeda and other nebulae.

Because we now know that ours is not the only galaxy in the universe, we make a simple distinction among the galaxies. We use the word Galaxy, with a capital G, to designate our own. Other galaxies are spelled with a small g.

Distances of the Galaxies

The nearest nebula to us is the Great Cloud of Magellan, about 150,000 light years away. Since the diameter of our Galaxy is itself over 100,000 light years, this nebula is not very far from us, astronomically speaking.

Because it is so close, the Great Cloud of Magellan was already known to the Persian astronomer, Al Sufi, one thousand years ago. He named it "the white ox." The first man to describe this nebula more fully was Antonio Pigafetta, a companion of Magellan during the first great sea voyage completely around the world. After the end of this gigantic undertaking in 1522, Pigafetta wrote a book about his experiences, in which he also gave an account of his observation of the "little mist," as he called the nebula. As a result, the "little mist" was given the name of Magellanic Cloud.

104. Horsehead nebula in Orion. *Its memorable shape has made this nebula justly famous. It is a dark nebula composed of gas and dust, the densest portions of which completely hide the stars behind them.*

It is not known how far it is to the most distant nebula. So far as we know, there are still more nebulae beyond the most distant one that we can see. With the most powerful telescope in the world, at Mount Palomar, we can explore space up to distances of billions of light years. Photographs taken with this telescope show that all space is strewn with galaxies, about a billion of them. They are similar to our own Galaxy and every one is composed of tens of billions of individual stars. It is expected that some of the stars in each of the galaxies may have planetary systems like that of our sun.

Some galaxies are alone in space, separated from their nearest neighbor galaxies by an average distance of some 2 million light years. Most of them, however, seem to be members of galactic groups.

One such group, found in the constellation called Hydra, or sea serpent, is among the remotest galactic systems known to us. The light which we receive from this group of galaxies started its journey over one billion years ago (the distance is over one billion light years). At that time life had barely appeared on the planet Earth. It was only when this light had almost completed its trip that life flourished on earth, men appeared, increased in intelligence, became interested in the stars, and built a telescope just in time to catch that travel-weary ray of light.

Some groups of galaxies are very thickly populated. For example, there are approximately 800 galaxies in the group to be found in the constellation Corona Borealis

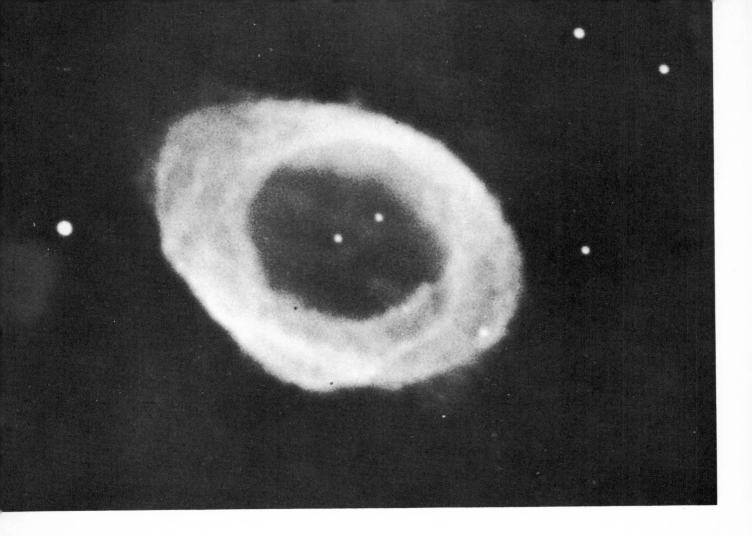

105. Ring nebula NGC 6720 in Lyra. *Nebulae of this type are called planetary only because they resemble the hazy globe of a planet through a small telescope. The ring is a cloud of gas that probably resulted from an eruption of the star at the center. An outer layer of the star is thought to have vaporized and expanded into space like a giant smoke ring.*

(Northern Crown), about 85 million light years from us. Our own Galaxy is part of what is known as the "local group." This is a small cluster of about twenty galaxies, which occupy a region of space about a million light years in diameter. It contains our Galaxy, the two Magellanic Clouds, and the Andromeda nebula.

Vast as our own Galaxy is, with its 100 billion stars, it is only a tiny speck in the greater vastness of space, one island universe among many.

A Model of the Universe It is easy to become bewildered in the contemplation of distances where one has to resort to the use of unfamiliar dimensions such as light years. Sir James Jeans, a famous English astronomer and physicist, developed a representation of the universe, which reduces the scale of the dimensions to make the proportions easier to grasp.

In Jeans' model, the orbit of the earth around the sun is represented by the head of a pin. The sun is a small grain of dust, about one-quarter of a thousandth of an inch in diameter, situated at the center of

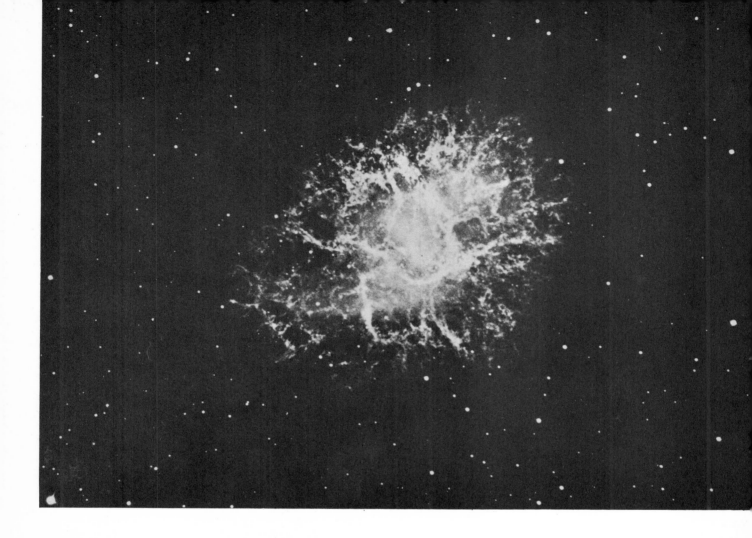

106. Crab nebula in Taurus. *This nebula is believed to have resulted from the gigantic explosion of a supernova in the year 1054 when it was reported that a brilliant new star had appeared in the heavens. It is one of the most powerful emitters of radio waves in the sky and has recently stimulated intensive research.*

the pinhead. On this scale, the star that is closest to us in our Galaxy is about 65 feet away. This star is Proxima, in the constellation Centaur.

If we picture all the stars in our Galaxy as grains of dust like our sun, then they will be scattered all about us, about 1300 feet apart. The entire Galaxy will be about the size of the American continent, from the Atlantic to the Pacific.

Compared to our Galaxy, then, our great sun is like a mere dot on a pinhead in relation to the American continent.

Continuing the model of the universe beyond the boundaries of our Galaxy, we find the next collection of grains of dust, the nearest galaxy to our own, at a distance of about 60,000 miles. If we now picture space as being inhabited by isolated clouds of dust, the size of the American continent, with about 60,000 miles between adjacent clouds, we will have a rough idea of the proportions of our visible universe. This is the part of the total universe accessible to us with the help of the telescope on Mount Palomar. Lost within one of these imagined continents of dust is our little earth, going round and round the head of a pin.

117

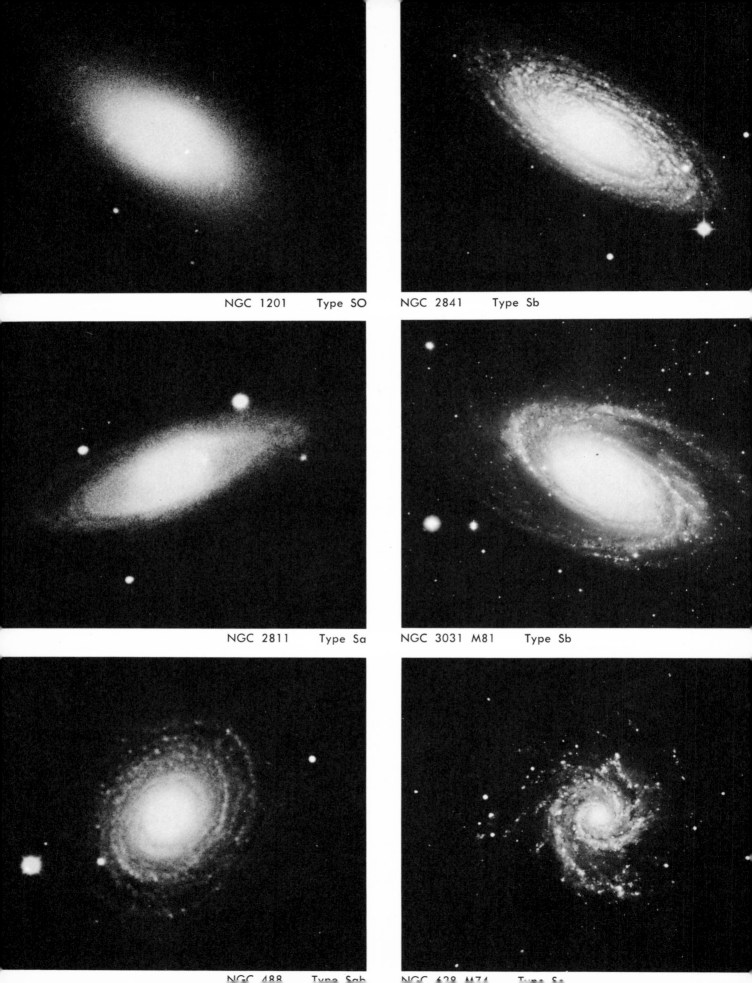

NGC 1201   Type SO

NGC 2841   Type Sb

NGC 2811   Type Sa

NGC 3031 M81   Type Sb

NGC 488   Type Sab

NGC 628 M74   Type Sc

How the Bodies of the Universe Were Formed

AFTER MEN had gained some insight into the arrangement of the heavenly bodies in space, it was natural to speculate next on how this arrangement might have been formed. Many theories have been proposed, but none has received general acceptance. We considered one of these theories previously as the basis for the story of the birth, life, and eventual death of our sun. This is called the *dust-cloud hypothesis*. Although there are many criticisms of it, it is probably the best guess we have today.

Origin of the Galaxies In this hypothesis, it is suggested that at one time the entire universe was filled with a cloud of ex-tremely fine dust and gas. All the matter in the universe, now contained in the stars and smaller bodies, was then dispersed throughout space.

There is evidence today that such dust clouds can exist. The Milky Way would look almost continuously bright if all the stars in it could be seen. Instead, there are dark patches here and there where the stars seem scattered more widely than else-where. There is good reason to believe that these dark patches are clouds of dust which obscure the stars behind them the way fog can dim or obliterate the lights of a city.

According to the hypothesis, the original universal dust cloud was not perfectly uni-form in density. There occurred in certain regions slightly more concentrated masses of dust. Since the particles in these denser regions were closer together than in other regions, the gravitational attraction be-tween particles was greater. This caused a tendency toward further concentration. The region of slightly greater density then shrank away from the surrounding cloud.

107. Types of galaxies. *Messier's list of nebulae numbered 103 by 1784. This was raised to 7840 in 1888 by Dreyer's New General Catalogue. The Index Catalogues, enlargements of the NGC, brought the total to over 13,000. The type designa-tions shown under the various representative galaxies refer to classifications made by Edwin Hubble, a renowned astronomer.*

119

The closer the particles came together, the more they attracted each other, thereby speeding up the rate of concentration.

Luck played a role in the formation of the denser clouds of dust. If the regions of dust concentration were too small, they did not contain enough matter to pull the concentrated particles away from the surrounding medium. The small cloud could then become torn and scattered and dissolve back into the universal cloud. If the region of concentration were large enough, however, the process of densification could continue, actually proceeding at a faster and faster rate as the particles coagulated.

It can be shown mathematically that clouds of dust and gas can subdivide into denser regions under such conditions. Furthermore, it can be shown that the mass of the coagulating region is greater if the mother cloud from which it forms is less dense. This is opposite to what one might expect intuitively. In the present case, the original dust cloud had so low a density that the mass of the newly formed subdivision was approximately the mass of a galaxy.

These condensing regions were the birthplaces of the galaxies. At this stage, the galaxy-to-be was still spread over incredibly large distances in space. Perfect homogeneity could not prevail over such great ranges. Differences in motion between various parts of the condensing mass gave rise to rotational movement of the mass as a whole. Larger masses rotated more sluggishly, smaller masses more rapidly.

If we scan the skies with a telescope today, we can find galaxies of different sizes, with different speeds of rotation and at different stages of evolution. In a mass of dust and gas which is not rotating, all particles are pulled uniformly toward the center. The mass assumes the shape of a spherical ball like the nebula found in the constellation Virgo, illustrated in figure 103b. If there is rotation, matter along the equator is flung outward like the skirts on a whirling dancer. This matter does not leave the galaxy, since the outward force, called *centrifugal,* is counterbalanced by the inward force, called *centripetal,* caused by gravitation. The mass expands around the equator and shrinks along the axis of rotation. This gives it a flattened shape.

When the speed of rotation is small, the ball is only slightly flattened like the nebula Messier 32 shown in figure 103a. If the speed is greater, the flattening is more pronounced. This produces a galaxy which appears like an ellipse when seen in profile. There are many such galaxies to be seen today. One example is the nebula NGC 3115 in figure 103d. If the speed of rotation is greater still, the flattening is also greater, the galaxy appearing to develop a thin edge. Because the centrifugal force tending to fling matter outward becomes so great, two huge arms along the outer rim may partially break away. This gives the spiral appearance which we encountered in our own Galaxy and in the Andromeda nebula shown in figure 91. Other spiral nebulae are illustrated in figure 103c (NGC 4565) and figure 103e (nebula of the constellation Corvus).

108. Man's deepest penetration of space. *At the center of the photograph is a faint cluster of galaxies in the constellation Pisces. The cluster is at a distance of over a billion light years, very near the limit of the observable universe.*

This accounts, if somewhat sketchily, for the formation of the broad outlines of the galaxies.

Birth of the Stars   Within the incompletely formed galaxy, stars were born by further condensations of dust and gas. As was stated above to explain the formation of the large galaxy from the thinly dispersed universal dust cloud, a denser cloud gives rise to condensation into smaller, but denser subdivisions. The galactic dust was much denser than the original dust cloud. There-

fore, the stars congealed as smaller, denser bodies. They, too, developed rotations about themselves, perhaps assisted by the rotation already existing in the parent galaxy.

Further shrinking of the star masses compressed the interiors, producing high pressures and temperatures. When the matter of the stars compacted sufficiently, nuclear reactions were started in the hot centers, furnishing a source of heat and light emitted by the stars. This was described by George Gamow, a well-known modern physicist. "After this process was over," wrote Gamow, "the original cold dark masses of the proto-galaxies were transformed into the shining star-swarms with which we are familiar."

It seems likely that stars are still being born. Although almost all the heavenly bodies are of more or less the same age, there appear to be some very new stars. Not all of the dust in space has congealed into celestial bodies. Dust clouds are still observed not only in the Milky Way, but also in the distant galaxies. As long as there is this interstellar dust, there is the material for the generation of stars. Some of the brightest stars in the sky are considered to be newborn, that is, only about 300 or 400 million years old.

When there is no longer any interstellar dust in a galaxy, no new stars can be born there. The spherical or slowly rotating galaxies are thought to be in just such a condition.

With the exception of these young stars, the rest of the bodies in the universe seem to be between 5 and 10 billion years old.

Birth of the Solar System   We started our story about how the heavenly bodies were formed with the origin of the galaxies. The first concern of earlier sky watchers was the origin of our own solar system, going back to the theory suggested as early as 1644 by René Descartes. After Newton had established the principles of gravitation, new theories were presented, such as that of Immanuel Kant in 1755. Kant, a

109. Center of globular star cluster Omega Centauri. *Globular clusters are compact groups of large numbers of stars. About 100 such clusters are known, most of them spherical in shape. Only two are easily seen with the naked eye, Omega Centauri (NGC 5139) and 47 Tucanae (NGC 104).*

great German philosopher, suggested that the sun had been surrounded by a gas envelope and that the planets had condensed from this gas. The French mathematician, Laplace, also advocated this notion. Later theorists suggested explanations based on solar magnetism; a clash between the sun and a comet, with planets the result of the fragments of the collision; a near collision between the sun and another star which created tidal waves on the sun, the waves rising so high that matter splashed out into space to freeze into planets; or previous existence of the sun as a member of a binary system (pair of stars) or even multiple system (more than two stars), with the planets somehow being the residue of the other members of the system. None of these theories is considered satisfactory. However, some modern scientists now favor a modification of Kant's idea.

They consider it possible that the sun was formed from a large cloud of dust and gas, just as was suggested in the case of stars in general. The cloud, in condensing, did not give birth only to the sun. Solid dust particles, colliding with each other, formed groups which became the planets. The hot center of the original dust cloud became the sun. This theory has some mathematical support.

There are two especially important features of this theory. The inclusion of dust along with gas in the mother cloud differed from the Kant hypothesis, which suggested that the cloud contained only gas. It is more reasonable that dust can collect into solid bodies than that gas can condense as required to form the planets. Also, the theory implies that the sun and the planets formed at approximately the same time, in a similar process of growth. It is even possible that the sun is a little younger than the planets.

This theory accounts for some of the characteristics of the solar system, but not all of them. Many difficulties still remain to be resolved.

Satellites are assumed to have come into being in a manner similar to that of the planets. Some of the peculiar motions of the satellites, however, also present problems not explained by the theory. The only conclusion to be drawn is that there is still much work to be done by the astronomers, mathematicians, and physicists before we can write a satisfactory biography of the bodies of the universe.

❈ ❈ ❈

Our imagination has roamed far and wide through the distant reaches of the universe. Understandably, we may have become dazed by the immense dimensions of space and the enormous sizes of some of its occupants. Our own little earth may seem shrunken and infinitesimal, as we return now to take a closer look at our home planet and study the history of its development. However, the true significance of earth is not found in its size. Earth is the home of man, the astronomer, who, alone, is capable of searching into the immensities of space, measuring its distances, and counting its suns.

110. Proposed soft-landing vehicle for moon trip.

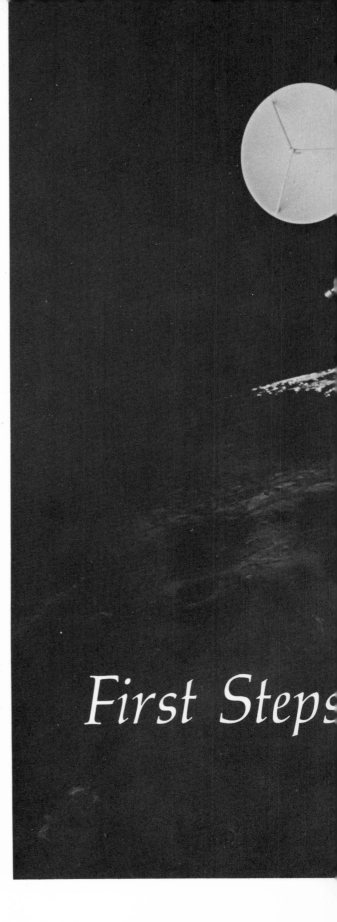

First Steps

Into Space

First Steps into Space Until very recently man has had to study the heavens with earthbound instruments, handicapped by distance and the veil of atmosphere that dims and distorts the light from planets and stars. Now powerful rockets have been developed to lift him away from the restraining pull of gravity. Guidance systems and measuring equipment have been improved to steer his path through space so that he may study the universe from a vantage point superior to those available to observatories on earth. Man has constructed electronic computers that act with lightning speed and extreme accuracy to control the flight of space vehicles, to plot their journey and make continual corrections of course beyond the capability of a human pilot. Along with these advances has come the refinement of radio communications necessary for contact with remote space vehicles. While exchanges by voice are maintained with men in space, information can stream back to earth, transmitted automatically from a multitude of instruments. Control signals are sent out to direct the spacecraft. Computers receive and analyze the information at a fantastic rate that would overwhelm an army of human telegraph operators. Man has gained the ability to leave his home planet.

Remarkable as these achievements are, the problems hindering space travel are so great that progress must be made in gradual, cautious steps. Over 250 years ago, Sir Isaac Newton supplied the essential mathematical tools and methods needed for space navigation. He made it possible to calculate the basic requirements of launching and directing a space ship. Modern science and engineering are only now beginning to meet these requirements.

Not only must the mechanical requirements of building and launching a space ship be met, but the dangers to men and materials must be discovered, weighed, and counteracted. Conditions in space were largely unknown until only a short time ago. Exploratory rockets have been shot off to measure temperatures, radiation levels, meteor impacts, magnetic fields, cosmic rays, the influence of solar flares, the effect of space environment on mice, monkeys, plants and other biological specimens, and a host of other factors. Dangerous concentrations of radiation were found, such as the Van Allen belt that is wrapped around the earth like a doughnut.

Forces needed to hurl heavy space vehicles off the earth are so great that enormous quantities of rocket fuel must be burned rapidly to provide the energy. This rapid burning is barely short of an explosion, yet it must be precisely controlled for reasons of safety and for accurate guidance of the vehicle. Chemists had to develop fuels with high energy content that were also susceptible to such precise control over burning rate.

The temperatures created by such fierce combustion and those generated by friction with the atmosphere at high speeds are often greater than conventional metals can normally withstand. New materials had to be created, special alloys, ceramics, plastics, and combinations such as *cermets*

126

111. Closeup views of the moon. *On July 31, 1964, in a magnificently successful flight of the United States Ranger 7 space vehicle, six television cameras transmitted to earth the first closeup photographs of the moon's surface. Unobscured by the earth's atmosphere, details are clear, disclosing craters as small as 30 feet in diameter and 10 feet deep. A and B were taken from altitudes of 11 and 3 miles, respectively. C was being transmitted at the instant of impact.*

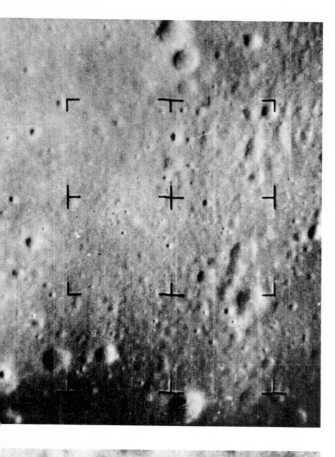

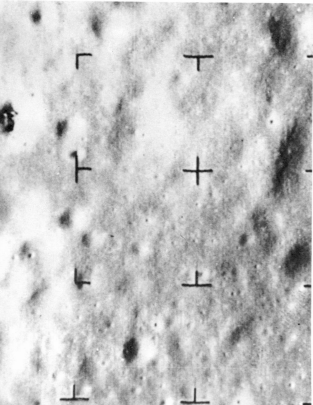

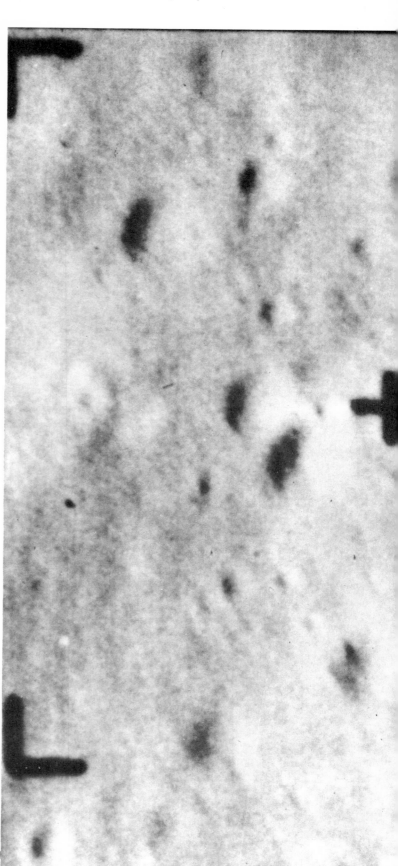

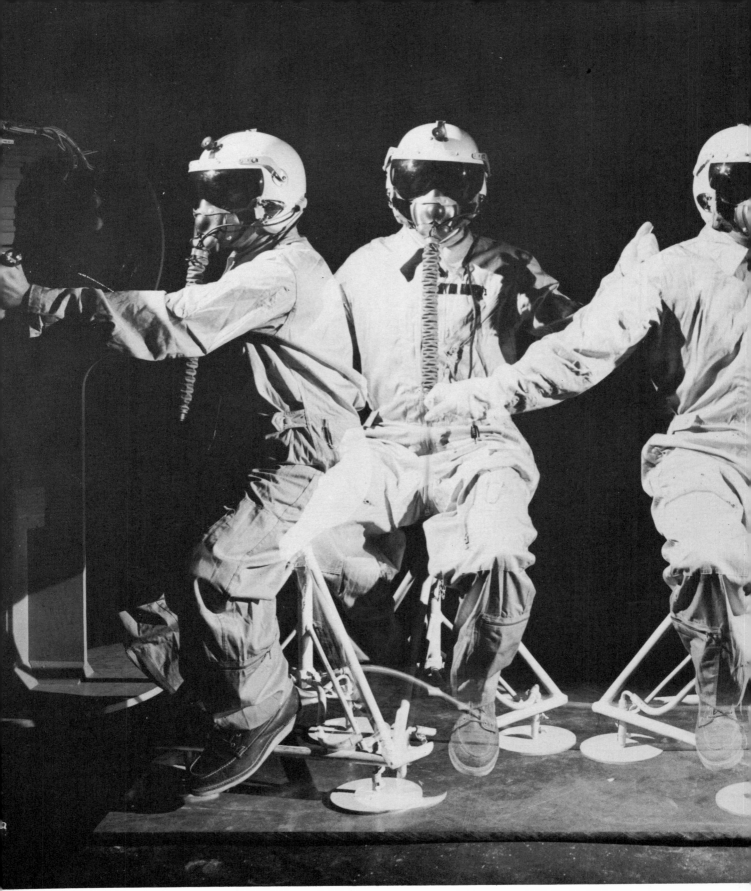

112. Working in space. *Men as well as nose cones must be tested. Stool on which man is sitting is floating on a cushion of compressed air, almost eliminating friction with the platform underneath. This simulates some of the problems of weightlessness. Man has just attempted to push on a tool at left to do repair work. Recoil has moved him across to other side of platform.*

113. Study of space vehicle flight characteristics. *A scale model of a possible spacecraft is set in the path of an air stream heated to 400°F to determine stability, control, and other aerodynamic behavior. Protective suit permits technician to inspect the model between tests without waiting for the tunnel to cool.*

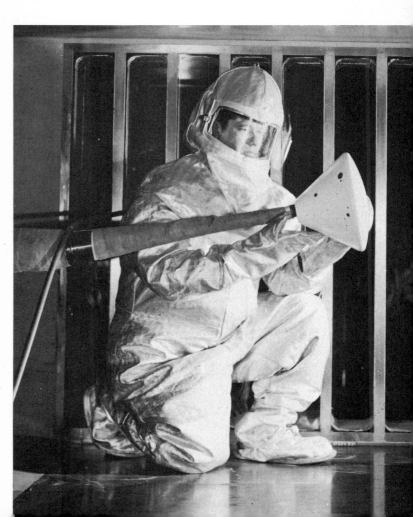

(*cer*amic-*met*al), unheard of only a few years ago.

During launch and re-entry severe vibrations place almost unbearable stresses on structures and endanger delicate apparatus. Intense research and development were required to produce stronger materials, new mechanical designs, new ways of mounting parts to absorb shock and vibration, new ways to measure stresses, and to replace fragile devices like glass vacuum tubes with such solid-state elements as transistors. Not only must all parts be sturdier than before, they must also be made smaller and lighter to reduce the burden on the rocket motor.

Man, too, is subjected to stress. He had to be tested for his ability to withstand vibration, shrieking noise, heat, tension, the sensation of weightlessness, the sensation of extreme heaviness brought on by rapid acceleration or deceleration, and even loneliness. Means had to be devised for feeding man in space, providing a breathable atmosphere, and disposing of wastes. Fit candidates were selected carefully and studied with exhaustive medical, biological, psychological, and physical tests to determine their responses to unearthly conditions. Even if man survived without apparent harm, could he function intelligently during and after his ordeal?

Then men and machinery had to be

114. Test of nose cone under re-entry conditions. *High velocity air in a wind tunnel simulates atmospheric friction encountered when a space vehicle returns to earth. Temperature rises abruptly to thousands of degrees, testing ability of nose cone shape and material to survive.*

130

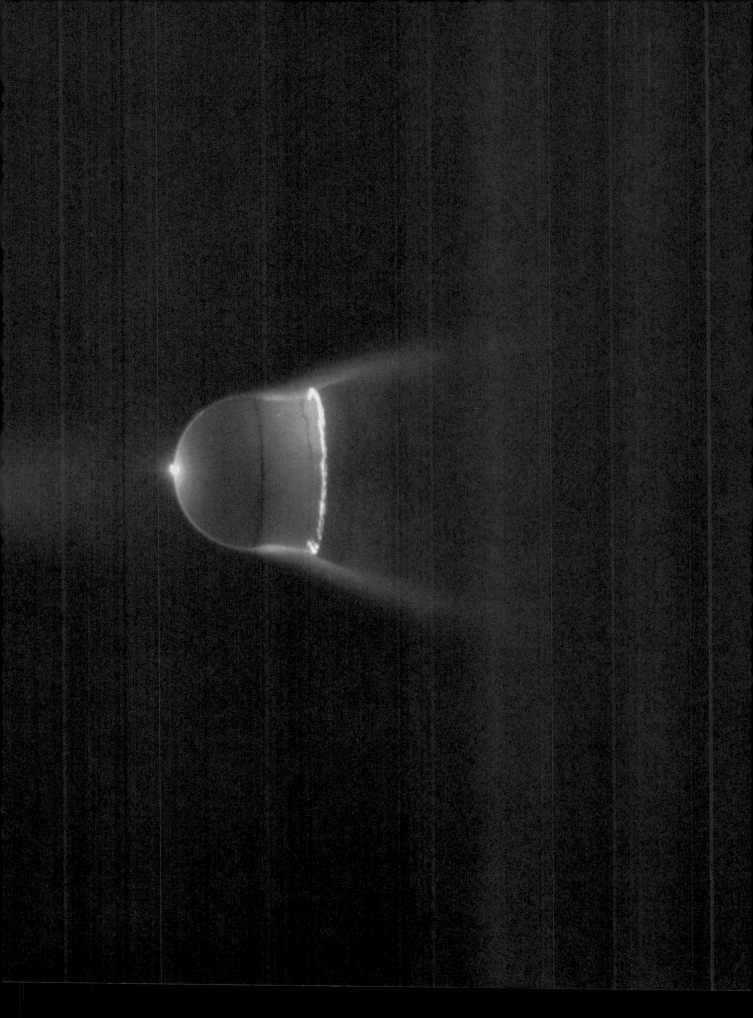

organized into a smoothly operating system with all possible errors and accidents foreseen and accounted for. Procedures were rehearsed over and over again, creating correct habits in the astronauts, conditioning them for their trials, while searching for flaws in the mechanisms.

Over all the human and engineering problems hovered the major problem of reliability. With human life and vast outlays of effort and money at stake, the rocket systems must be made to work with as great a certainty as possible. The systems are incredibly complex and contain thousands of parts. The more parts there are, the greater the chance that one vital part may fail. Combined with an engineering effort to make parts of higher quality and better design was an extension of mathematical techniques for analyzing the probabilities of such a failure. Armed with this statistical data, engineers could redesign valves, levers, switches, circuit components, and the many other parts for greater reliability; they could also invent tests to screen out potentially faulty units. Component parts and systems were put through their paces in wind tunnels, furnaces, vacuum chambers, freezers, shakers, centrifuges, drop towers, rocket sleds, and other implements of torture which simulated possible launch conditions or space environments.

115, 116. Launching of Scout space vehicle. *The Scout is a four-stage, solid-fuel vehicle used for a number of exploratory flights. In launching position at left, the spacecraft at right lifts off with a shattering roar, trailing clouds of expanding gases.*

132

After scientific and engineering ingenuity had set the stage for space travel, unmanned rockets were launched. Then unmanned orbiting vehicles were sent aloft to circle the globe as man-made moons. Finally, man rode a space ship in orbit around the earth some hundreds of miles above the surface, first from the Soviet Union, then from the United States. Rockets have landed on the moon and soared past Venus; photographs and measurements have been transmitted back to earth by dozens of vehicles with new information about the shape of our own earth, the appearance to the far side of the moon, as well as tentative data about the space beyond.

Despite the great excitement and expectations of the general public, the next steps will not be easy. In addition to the risk to life involved in each space venture, space explorers are faced with the vast emptiness of the universe. Only our nearest planetary neighbors are close enough for space ships to reach within a reasonable travel time of the order of months. Even this would require speeds that may seem fantastic. At the speed of light, the fastest speed of all, it would take 4 years to journey to the nearest star beyond our solar system.

It is foolhardy to predict the farthest point in space to which man may travel. We are only on the threshold of the space age and the stimulation of military competition is unfortunately still great. The immediate limits are set by the boldness of man and his ability and willingness to meet the challenge and pay the costs.

117. Fiery re-entry of Titan nose cone. *No labora-tory test, this is a photograph of the re-entry into the earth's atmosphere of a Mark IV nose cone of a Titan ICBM (intercontinental ballistic missile).*

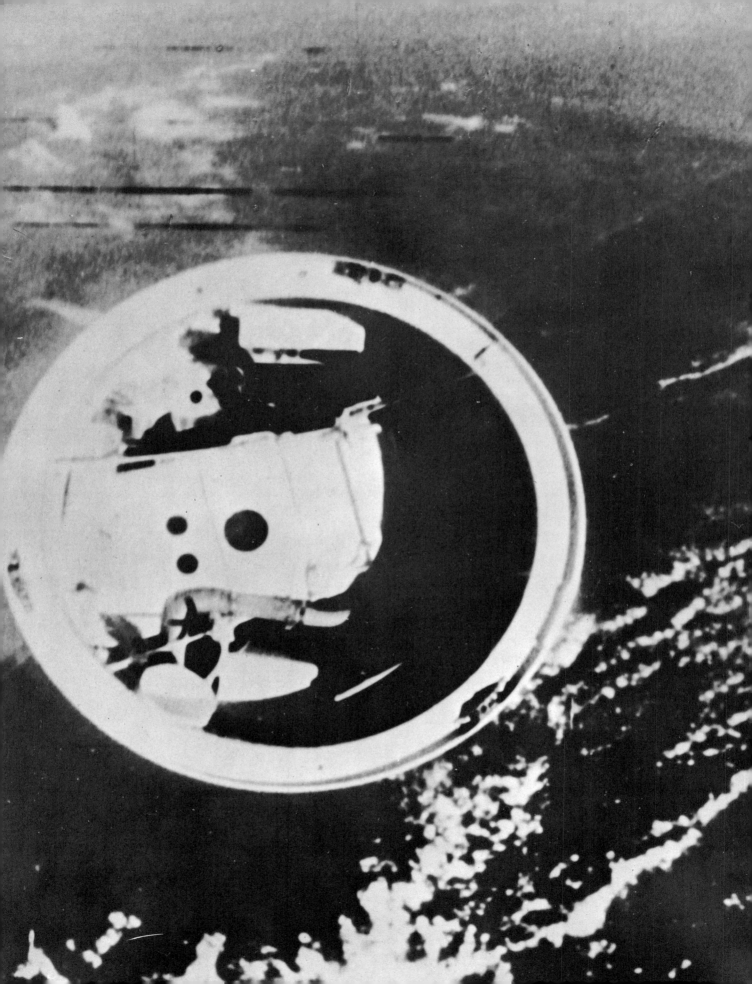

118-122. Picture sequence from space. *A camera records the gradual falling away of the booster rocket that carried the instrument capsule hundreds of miles above the earth. Below, the coast of Florida is visible. Although most of the ground details are obscured by the clouds of a weather front (lower right), the curvature of the earth is clearly visible.*

123. Practicing moon landings. *Pilot hovers over surface of moon in simulation tests. His controls are really a type of computer that calculates and records his ability to execute the braking maneuvers necessary for lunar landings.*

BELOW:

124. Center for biological studies on the moon. *Activities on the moon may be housed in self-inflating domes. The absence of outside atmospheric pressure permits a small amount of enclosed gas to expand more than on earth, and the low gravitational pull of the moon·makes the supported structure lighter in weight.*

AT RIGHT:

125. Two halves of a proposed space station. *The large "pods" sitting on their launching vehicles may be joined later in orbit above the earth to form a way station or space motel. Travelers can pause here before proceeding to a final destination.*

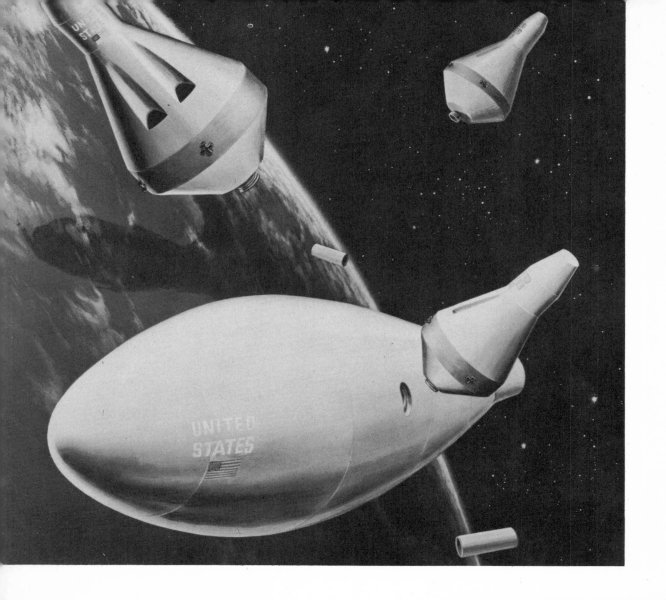

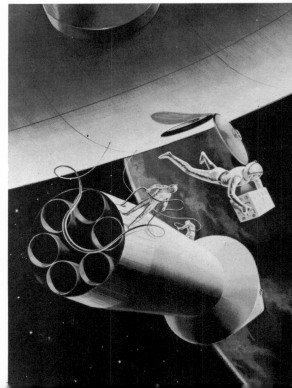

126-130. Assembly of a space station. *Two large pod-shaped housings are ferried into position by small spacecraft to be connected by a large boom 100 feet long when fully extended. Station will be the scene of such activities as refueling of engines, repair of nearby unmanned satellites, and scientific studies.*

140

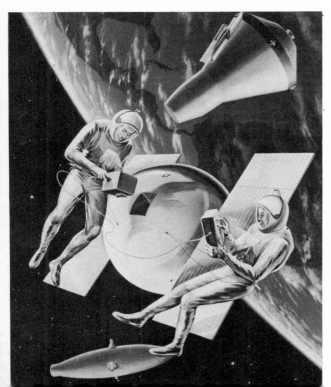

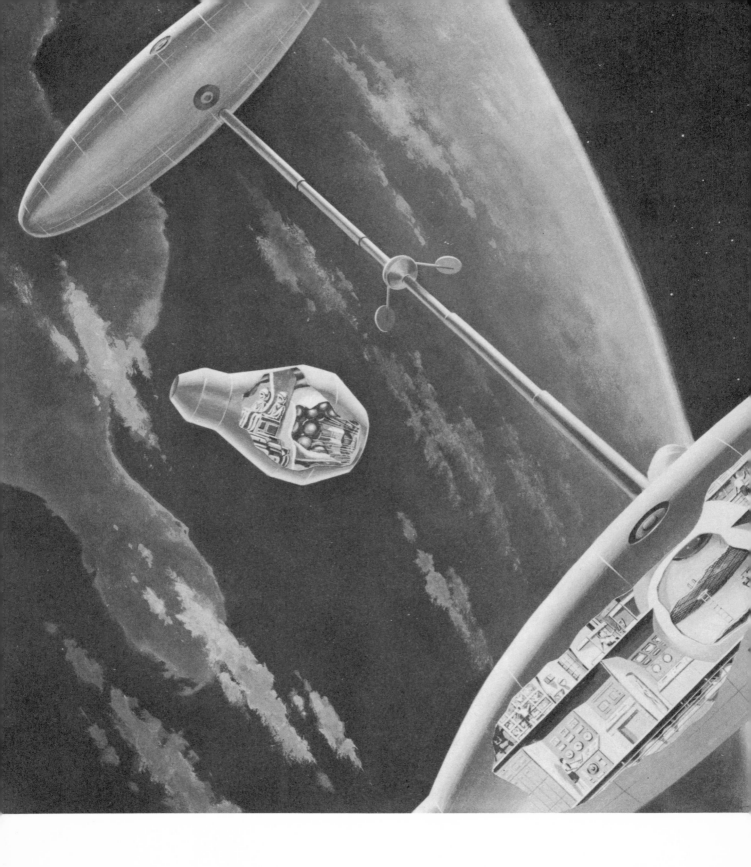

131, 132. Space operations. *The completed space station revolves end over end like a tumbling dumbbell, the centrifugal force created acting like an artificial gravity to avoid weightlessness. Men leaving station through air lock are members of training group for future astronauts.*

Glossary

Airglow. A weak glow appearing in the night sky. It is caused by radiant energy from the sun.

Altitude. In astronomy, the angular height of a body above the horizon. For example, a star has an altitude of 30° when the angle between the star, observer, and horizon is 30°.

Andromeda nebula. A galaxy or vast cloud of dust, gas, and stars in the constellation Andromeda. Known as Messier 31, the nebula is visible to the naked eye.

Apogee. That point in the moon's orbit which is farthest from the earth. It is also used for other orbiting bodies, such as the planets, comets, and the orbits of artificial satellites. The opposite of perigee.

Asteroid. Any of the small minor planets—there are more than 1500 known—which revolve about the sun between the orbits of Mars and Jupiter.

Astrology. A system which claims to predict events from the positions of heavenly bodies, and to disclose the "influence" that such bodies exert on human affairs.

Astronomy. The science which deals with the heavenly bodies, their size, motion, distance, relative position, and chemical composition.

Atmosphere. The layer of gas or gases surrounding a heavenly body, such as the earth or another planet.

Axis (planetary). An imaginary straight line around which a planet rotates.

Binary system. Two stars which appear to revolve about one another, but which actually revolve about a common center. They are held by mutual gravitational attraction.

Centigrade. Temperature measured on a thermometer scale on which water freezes at 0° and boils at 100° at standard atmospheric pressure. *See* Fahrenheit.

Centrifugal. The force with which a body moving in a curve pulls against the restraint that holds it in this path.

Centripetal. That force which prevents a revolving object from flying off on a tangent. It is equal but opposite in direction to centrifugal force.

Chemical reaction. The process by which different substances act on one another producing chemical change.

Chronometer. An extremely accurate instrument for measuring time; especially, one used at sea for determining longitude.

Comet. A loose swarm of particles moving in an elongated elliptical orbit around the sun. The visible part of a comet is a gas envelope that surrounds its nucleus and trails off as a long tail. *See* Halley's Comet; Non-periodic comet; Periodic comet.

Constellation. A recognizable group of stars named for reference and identification. By international agreement, a total of 88 are recognized.

Copernican system. The idea, established by Polish astronomer Nicholas Copernicus in 1543, that the earth and other planets revolve around the sun.

Corona. The outer gaseous layer surrounding the sun. It is visible to the naked eye only during a total eclipse of the sun.

Cosmic rays. Particles of very high energy which emanate from the sun or any other star and speed through space. When cosmic-ray primaries collide with the earth's atmosphere, they create secondary particles which reach us at ground level.

Crater (moon). A circular walled formation on the moon's visible surface, ranging in size from a tiny pit to 200 miles across. The origin of the lunar craters is not definitely known.

Day. The length of time it takes the earth to rotate once on its axis. A day is measured from noon to noon or midnight to midnight.

Density. The amount of matter contained in a given space, expressed as mass per unit volume.

Dwarf stars. A class of small, faint stars which have used up all their hydrogen. Although they emit relatively little light, they may have high densities.

Earth. The third planet in order of distance from the sun. It is shaped like a ball that is slightly flattened at the poles, weighs 6,000 million, million, million tons, and is a distance of 93 million miles from the sun.

Eclipse. The total or partial blocking from view of a celestial object by another one passing in front of it. *See* Lunar eclipse; Solar eclipse.

Element. A substance which cannot be broken down by chemical means into simpler substances. Examples: gold, oxygen, lead, chlorine.

Ellipse. The closed curve formed when a circular cone is cut through at an angle to the cone's axis. The orbit of a planet moving around the sun is elliptical—that is, it is shaped like a flattened circle.

Elliptical orbit. The usual path of one celestial body around a second body under the influence of gravitational attraction, such as that of the earth around the sun.

Equator. The great "circle" around the earth, lying midway between the poles, from which north and south latitudes are measured. An imaginary plane through the equator is at right angles to the earth's axis.

Equinox. One of the two times during the year when the sun is directly over the equator, making the hours of daylight and darkness very nearly equal all over the earth. The winter equinox occurs about March 21 and the autumnal equinox about September 21.

Fahrenheit. A thermometer scale on which water freezes at 32° and boils at 212°. It is named for the physicist who devised it. *See* Centigrade.

Field stars. Those stars which appear in the field of view of a telescope.

Fireballs. Exceptionally large meteors which become incandescent when they enter the earth's atmosphere. They become visible at a height of from 80 to 100 miles above the ground. *See* Meteor.

Galaxy. The name given to our huge, rotating, pin-wheel-like star system, of which the sun and earth are but small parts. The galaxy is shaped like a flattened disk with a central bulge (the middle parts we see as the Milky Way), has as many as 100,000 million stars, contains great clouds of dust and gas out of which new stars are constantly being formed, and has a diameter of about 80,000 light-years. There are at least 10,000 million galaxies within the range of today's telescopes.

Gravitation. The force of attraction which one mass exerts on another, no matter how large or small.

Gyroscope. A rapidly spinning wheel or disk, mounted so that its axis of spin is free to swivel in all directions with minimum friction with its surroundings. The device resists any change in the direction of its axis.

Halley's Comet. The famous periodic comet which, on an average, completes its long elliptical orbit around the sun once every 76 years. It is named after Edmond Halley who observed it in 1682 and correctly predicted its return in 1758. *See* Periodic comet.

Helium. An inert gaseous element which is the second most abundant element in the universe. The energy in stars comes from the conversion of hydrogen into helium.

Jupiter. The largest planet in our solar system, fifth in order of distance from the sun. It has a diameter of 89,000 miles and boasts 12 moons.

Light-year. The distance that light travels in one year, at a velocity of about 186,000 miles a second. One light-year equals about six trillion miles.

Lunar eclipse. The earth's shadow cast upon the moon, occurring when the earth passes between the sun and the moon.

Magnetic storm. A period during which violent changes in electric currents in the ionosphere interrupt short-wave radio, long-distance telephone, and television communications. Such a "storm" is often followed by increased intensity of light from areas of the sun near sunspots.

Mars. A comparatively small planet in our solar system—half as large as the earth—which immediately follows the earth in order of distance from the sun. Because of the abundance of iron oxide in its soil, Mars appears reddish in color. It has two tiny moons.

Mercury. The nearest planet to the sun, and less than half the size of the earth. No life can exist on Mercury, because of a very thin atmosphere and extreme temperatures.

Meteor. Stone, stone-iron, and iron fragments that race in swarms or as lone objects through space, circling the sun. Also known as a "shooting star," a meteor usually flares into a vapor before it reaches the earth, due to the heat produced by its rapid passage through the air.

Meteorite. A meteor which survives its journey through the earth's atmosphere without vaporizing and strikes the ground. The largest one known, called Ahnighito, was found in Greenland and weighs 34 tons.

Milky Way. A luminous band of light arching across the night sky. The effect is caused by our looking into our galaxy edge on, so that millions of stars appear to be crowded together.

Month. The period of a complete revolution of the moon around the earth, usually 28 to 30 days.

Moon. The earth's only satellite, the moon is 1/4 the earth's size and its volume is 1/50th of the earth's. It lacks an atmosphere, and its surface consists of craters, steep, sharp mountains—whose rock has not been eroded, due to the lack of wind and water—and vast plains which are probably composed of very fine dust. The moon controls the earth's tides, and it causes solar eclipses when it passes across the sun's disk. Other planets have moons which differ greatly in size, composition, and surface features from our own. *See* Craters; Eclipse; Lunar eclipse; Satellite; Solar eclipse; Tide.

Mount Palomar. An observatory in California possessing the world's largest reflecting telescope, with a mirror 200 inches in diameter.

Neap tide. When the high tide is lowest. A neap tide is caused by the sun and moon attracting the earth's ocean water from two opposing directions.

Nebula. Glowing patches in the sky, named for their hazy appearance. They are now known to be a variety of phenomena, such as clouds of dust and gas, star clusters, or distant galaxies.

Neptune. The fourth largest of the planets and the eighth in order of distance from the sun. It is a twin planet to Uranus in terms of size and motion.

Non-periodic comet. A comet which passes the earth only once and then disappears, apparently forever, because of an irregular or distended orbit.

Northern lights. A glow of colored lights in the northern skies, caused by charged particles streaming from the sun and entering earth's atmosphere. Also known as Aurora Borealis. In southern skies they are known as Aurora Australis.

Nova. A star that for reasons not yet fully understood bursts into brilliance. Within a few days a typical nova may become 60,000 times brighter than usual, but after a few months or years it returns to its pre-nova state.

Orbit. The path which a planet or other celestial

object traces as it circles another. The earth and other planets each have their own orbit around the sun. The moon travels in an orbit around the earth.

Penumbra. The less-dark part of the shadow cast during an eclipse. The darker inner core of the shadow is known as the umbra.

Perigee. That point in the orbit of the moon, planets, comets, or artificial satellite which is nearest the earth. Opposite of apogee.

Periodic comet. A comet which travels an elliptical orbit about the sun and is visible on earth at regular intervals. *See* Halley's Comet.

Photometer. An instrument that measures the intensity of light, as from the stars and planets.

Photosphere. The apparent surface of the sun. The temperature of the photosphere is about 6000°C.

Planet. One of the nine large bodies that revolve about the sun in our solar system. In order of distance from the sun, the nine planets are: Mercury, Venus, Earth, Mars, Jupiter, Saturn, Uranus, Neptune, Pluto.

Planetoid. A comparatively small heavenly body in orbit around the sun between Mars and Jupiter. Also known as minor planets, there are some 1500 which are known to date. *See* Asteroid.

Pluto. A planet smaller than earth and the ninth in order of distance from the sun. It is the least known planet because of its small size and remote position.

Proto-star. The partial concentration of various particles and dust which may eventually form a star as condensation takes place.

Ring nebula. A cloud of dust and gas which appears as a ring surrounding a bright central star.

Rings of Saturn. Thin, flat, circular clouds, probably of ice particles, that ring Saturn like a hat brim. The diameter of the rings is about 172,000 miles. They are less than 10 miles thick.

Satellite. A smaller body which revolves about a larger one. The moon is a satellite of the earth.

Saturn. The second largest planet in the solar system and sixth in order of distance from the sun. The average surface density is less than that of water but its main glory lies in its rings, one of the most beautiful sights in the heavens.

Solar eclipse. The blocking out of the sun from view due to the moon passing between the earth and the sun.

Solar prominences. Glowing masses of hot gases erupted from the sun's surface. They are visible without special instruments only during a total solar eclipse.

Solar system. Our planetary family, including the sun, the planets and their satellites, the asteroids, comets, and meteors.

Specific gravity. Under standard conditions, the ratio of the density of a substance to that of water. The earth's average specific gravity is 5.5, meaning that the earth weighs five-and-a-half times as much as a globe of water of equal size.

Spectroscope. An optical instrument that separates light into its individual colors or spectra. The chemical composition of a star can be deduced from the spectrum of its starlight.

Spiral galaxy. A group of stars forming a galaxy with a dense center and less dense spiral arms winding outward.

Spring tide. When high tide is highest.

Star. A luminous celestial body of hot gases such as our sun. Astronomically, the sun is a star of average brightness, size, and probable age.

Sun. The incandescent celestial body around which the earth and other planets revolve, and from which they receive light and heat. The sun's surface temperature is 11,000°F, and its inner temperature is 35,000,000°F.

Sunspot. A great, dark spot on the face of the sun (some measure up to 150,000 miles across) consisting of a whirlpool of hot gas. The spot appears dark in contrast with the surrounding hotter zones.

Telescope. An optical instrument with curved lenses or mirrors that magnify the image of distant objects.

Tide. The rise and fall of the earth's oceans caused by the attraction of the moon and sun.

Universe. All matter everywhere, including all celestial bodies, seen or unseen.

Uranus. The seventh planet in order of distance from the sun. It ranks as a giant, having a diameter of nearly 30,000 miles, but it cannot be seen without a powerful telescope.

Venus. The second planet in order of distance from the sun, and similar in size to the earth. It is much brighter than anything else in the sky apart from the sun and moon, but it is so completely hidden by a dense atmosphere that its surface cannot be seen.

Weightlessness. The apparent absence of the earth's gravitational pull, such as occurs during the orbital flight of space capsules. It is a consequence of free fall and may also be felt in a runaway elevator.

Zenith. The point on the celestial sphere directly above the observer's head. It is the opposite of nadir.

Zodiac. An imaginary belt in the heavens which encircles an observer on earth like the rim of a wheel about its hub. The path of the sun, as it appears to move around the earth, defines the middle of the belt. The region enclosed by the belt contains the orbits of the moon and all the principal planets.

PHOTOGRAPHIC CREDITS

Index

Index

Recent Developments

AND ADDITIONAL INFORMATION

ASTRONOMY, cosmology (the science of the past, present, and future of the universe as a whole), and geophysics (physics dealing with the earth) are presently in a state of intense and exciting activity. The ferment is a result of new data gathered in recent years by a variety of instruments: some older, like the giant optical telescopes stationed on isolated mountaintops, and some ultramodern, like the broad antennas built just during the last decade for radio astronomers or the space probes launched by rockets which grow more powerful each year. Certain discoveries have challenged established physical theories and may necessitate the reappraisal of strongly held ideas.

Radio and X-ray Sources in Space Radio telescopes with large, saucer-shaped antennas over 200 feet in diameter have been used to scan the sky and have detected increasing numbers of sources of radio waves. Some of these sources have proved to be previously known stars or even planets (Jupiter and Venus) visible also to optical telescopes. Other sources appear unrelated to any objects in the astronomer's catalogues. Thousands of small areas in the sky are now known to be radiating energy on radio wave lengths.

Radio frequencies are lower than those of light and are therefore generated by different processes; these involve lower energy transformations than the processes that produce visible light. Waves of lower frequency (longer wave length) can penetrate the clouds of dust and gas that obscure parts of the universe from conventional telescopes. Moreover, optical telescopes are effective only when nights are clear and dark, but radio telescopes can be operated day and night and under any weather conditions

Radio telescopes not only detect energy from objects in space, they also supply clues to what these objects may be and by what means the energy they emit is released. Just as optical telescopes coupled with spectroscopes can be used to analyze the fre-

quencies of light emitted by stars, thereby allowing the astronomer to estimate stellar temperatures and chemical compositions, so radio telescopes also distinguish the frequencies of received signals. The existence of hydrogen in the vast, supposedly empty spaces between stars was demonstrated by this means. The spinning electron in a hydrogen atom is known to change its spin about once in some 11 million years. Because there are so many hydrogen atoms in a cloud of gas of even very low density, there are always multitudes of electrons in the process of changing their spins. This switching is accompanied by the emission of radio waves of a distinct wave length of 21.1 centimeters. With ingenious circuit devices, engineers are able to screen out these faint emissions from the background of noisy radio crackle. This accomplishment has permitted the mapping of the density of hydrogen throughout our galaxy, revealing the presence of clouds of gas which rotate about the center of the galaxy like the more solid members of the galactic family. This also gives a more accurate picture of the amount of matter suspended in space. In a different but analogous manner, the chemical grouping called the *hydroxyl radical* was observed in space for the first time. This radical contains one atom of oxygen attached to one atom of hydrogen.

Radio-frequency energy provides hints regarding the activity of stars and other matter in space, apart from the primary nuclear reactions that supply the energy to make the stars burn brightly. Our sun is a strong broadcaster of radio waves of various wave lengths. Bursts of radio waves that accompany sunspot eruptions have helped to create a clearer understanding of the sun's behavior. Other information concerning the sun and more distant stars is received in the form of x-rays.

X-ray sources were detected by hurling space laboratories above the earth's atmosphere. Since the atmosphere acts as a shroud about the earth, it completely absorbs the soft (relatively low energy) x-rays and prevents their detection on the ground.

Russian photograph of the back side of the moon. *Transmitted back to earth on July 20, 1965, this* *picture shows the equatorial and northern parts of the back side of the moon.*

These x-rays serve to fill in other gaps in our knowledge of the universe. From the vastness that surrounds us we are a perpetual host to visitors—light, radio waves, x-rays, cosmic rays, meteorites, neutrinos—all bearing messages in strange languages that we struggle to decipher.

Related to the radio telescopes are the radar telescopes. *Radar* consists of pulses of high-frequency radio waves which are bounced off a target to return as instructive echoes. The echoes carry information in several forms. The time it takes a pulse to reach the target and return at a speed of 186,000 miles per second is an accurate measure of the distance to the target. By this means the distance to the moon was found to be 238,866 miles with an estimated possible error of only about one mile in the measurement. Through a detailed analysis of the returning pulses radar can also indicate the size of a body, the roughness and general character of the reflecting surface, and even its temperature. In 1946, meteor showers, blotted out from visual observation by dense clouds, were followed by radar. Since then radar has been used to study the orbits and velocities of such showers.

Because radar signals become weaker and more dispersed as they travel farther from earth, the limitations of our present equipment restrict this method to a study of only our immediate neighbors. Larger and more versatile radar telescopes are now being designed and constructed, so that man can chart the solar system in greater detail and with finer precision than ever before possible.

Although radio astronomy was born in 1931, when Karl G. Jansky, an engineer at Bell Labora-

tories in New Jersey, first demonstrated that radio signals were reaching us from the Milky Way, its major development has taken place since World War II. The many advances in radio and radar stimulated by the war effort laid the necessary technical foundation for rapid growth. Despite the short time it has been in existence, this new science has already made major contributions to astronomical

Ranger 8 photograph of the moon's surface. *This picture was taken by Ranger 8 at an altitude of 151* *miles above the surface of the moon, 2 minutes and 15 seconds before impact.*

Walk in space. *Astronaut Edward White is seen leaving his Gemini 4 spacecraft, floating away from the craft with the arc of the earth behind him, and using his oxygen gun to maneuver around the ship.*

research. Probably the most striking was the discovery of quasars.

Quasars When it was discovered that thousands of spots in the sky were sending out radio signals, astronomers pointed their great optical telescopes toward these spots for further investigation. In many instances they could see nothing, which led to speculation that there are radio stars—too cool to emit enough light or too far away to be visible. In other instances, they found dimly glowing objects, such as nebulae of various shapes; these were of considerable interest but not unfamiliar in type. In 1960, however, Rudolph Minkowski photographed a radio source of intense energy with the 200-inch telescope on Mount Palomar. By measuring the shift of the red lines in the spectrum with a spectroscope, calculating the speed of the source necessary to produce the very large shift, and then using the relationship between speed and distance, Minkowski reached the startling conclusion that the radio source must be about 5 billion light-years away, the most distant object known at that time. In 1964, Maarten Schmidt repeated the astronomical adventure by confirming that another radio source was even farther away, a distance of about 7 billion light-years. This was the

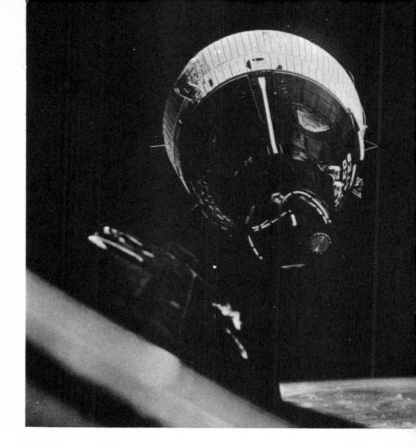

Man's first rendezvous in space. *The historic meeting of two space capsules 160 miles above the earth. Both photographs show the nose cone of Gemini 7 as seen from Gemini 6 (visible above in the lower left). Each capsule was maneuvered by a pair of United States Astronauts.*

most distant known object in the universe. It also seemed to be the fastest-moving object yet discovered, rushing away from us toward the outermost edge of the cosmos at the incredible rate of 76,000 miles per second. Just recently, Dr. Schmidt has discovered one whose speed is 149,000 miles per second.

A few dozen of these unusual radio sources have now been listed, corresponding to no known type of astronomical entity. Because no one knows what they are, they are called quasi-stellar radio sources, *quasi* meaning apparently but perhaps not really, and *stellar* meaning a star. For short, they are named *quasars*.

Quasars are a revolutionary arrival in astronomy, and perhaps in other sciences as well. Their unprecedented characteristics raise questions that may result in revisions of basic principles. For example, for quasars to be visible to a telescope with the most sensitive photographic apparatus available from a distance of 42,000,000,000,000,000,000,000 miles, it has been calculated that the source must radiate about 100 times as much energy as the combined total of all the 100 billion stars in our Milky Way. How can such unheard-of quantities of energy be produced? Theories to explain this have been forthcoming; one states that far-off galaxies had collided with a cosmic crash, and another that an enormous mass of matter had collapsed into a superdense ball by mutual gravitational attraction of all the parts, which increased rapidly and explosively as the matter compacted into closer contact. No one really knows, but the explanations seem inadequate. Some astrophysicists are beginning to question whether the relationship between the speed of a star and its distance from us is truly valid that far away. Are there processes unknown to us that release fantastic amounts of energy in comparison with those within the range of our experience? It is hoped and even expected that quasars will prove to be not merely unsettling, but rather an exciting step forward to a better understanding of the structure of the universe.

In particular, the increasing accumulation of data from radio astronomy and other fields may soon resolve the problem of deciding how our universe came to be the way it is and what are the expectations for its future. Currently, the choice lies among three theories which seem to fit the evidence, so far as it is known. These are referred to as the *Big-Bang Theory,* the *Theory of the Oscillating Universe,* and the *Steady-State Theory.*

The Big-Bang Theory   Estimates of the age of the earth, the sun, and the stars, usually by deduction from the known rate of decay of radioactive materials, tend to show them all about the same age— some 5 to 10 billion years. Furthermore, the red shift in the spectrum of light from stars indicates that the universe is expanding in all directions, the speed with which celestial objects are racing outward being proportional to their distance from us (Hubble's Law). Using their present velocity and position, their past velocities and positions can be calculated, back to times when they were much closer together than they are now. These calculations can be carried back in time to the point where

Mariner 4 photographs of Mars. *This composite overlay shows the areas of Mars photographed by Mariner 4.*

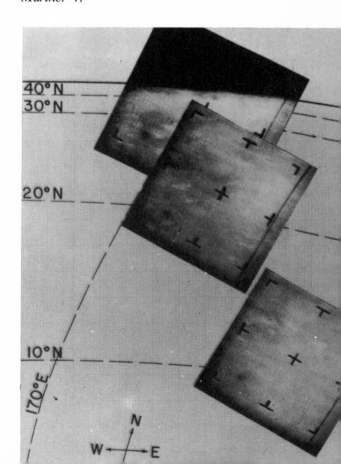

Close-up of Mars. *This photograph taken by Mariner 4 shows the surface of Mars, covering an area of 170 miles. Large and small craters are easily distinguished.*

all matter in the universe might once have been consolidated in a single enormous globe of energy, about 15 billion years ago, according to calculations. The relative agreement of all these estimates is part of the support for the Big-Bang Theory of the universe.

This theory proposes that the original ball of energy exploded and thus started the outward expansion, one stage of which we see now. This will continue for all time, matter dispersing more and more, everything flying farther and farther apart. Local clusters like our solar system or our galaxy will tend to travel somewhat as a unit, held together by gravitational attraction.

The Big-Bang Theory does not contain answers to the questions of how the big ball first came to be or what was there before. The Theory of the Oscillating Universe does not have to face this difficulty.

The Theory of the Oscillating Universe It is the natural tendency of material bodies, in the absence of other influences, to collect together by mutual gravitational attraction. As the universe expands, as a result of some explosive kick far back in time, the fleeing bodies are still attracting each other by their gravitation. (This pull acts like a rein on a runaway horse.) Slowly but surely, their outward flight is being lessened, until one day in the distant future they will actually be brought to a stop, their direction of motion will reverse, and the gravitational strings will reel them back together again. As they approach each other, the gravitational attraction will increase rapidly, since it rises twice as fast as the distance decreases between the attracting bodies. In the last stages they will collide, press together, become superdense; then the tremendous heat and pressure will result in violent reactions and an explosion of unimaginable proportions. The universe will begin to expand again.

What determines whether the Big Bang occurs just once or whether the universe oscillates is the amount and distribution of matter. If enough matter exists in the universe and if it is dense enough, the gravitational attraction will be great enough to retrieve the scattering pieces. If not, the pieces will scatter far, the gravitational force weakening as the spaces widen, until the attraction is too slight, the distances too vast, and the speeds too high for the Humpty Dumpty universe to be put back together again.

The Theory of the Oscillating Universe does not need to answer the question, "What came before?" This is the way it has always been and this is the way it will always be, as far back or as far forward in time as you care to go. The alternative theory, the Steady-State Theory, also states that things are now as they were and as they will be, but with a difference.

The Steady-State Theory

This theory proposes that the average density of matter in the universe is unchanging, that the skies were always pretty much as they are now, and that they will remain so. There are motions, of course, and the parts of the universe are racing away from each other, but as they separate, new matter is created to fill the voids—that is, there is continuous creation going on.

Although at first glance this seems contrary to all experience, the proponents of the theory calculate that the amount of matter that must be created to maintain a steady-state universe is so minute that we would not notice it anyway. All that is required is the spontaneous appearance of a few hydrogen atoms per city block every million years or so.

While scientists ponder the grand design of the cosmos, the pace of space exploration increases almost daily. Discoveries are not relegated to technical journals but become headlines or feature stories in newspapers.

Recent Developments

Among the most spectacular recent events were the photographing of the moon and Mars by United States space ships—Rangers 7, 8, and 9 and Mariner 4—the "walking" in space by the Russian cosmonaut Alexei Leonov and the American Edward White, the eight-day orbital flight of astronauts Gordon Cooper and Charles Conrad, and the latest Russian photograph of the back side of the moon. Ranger 9 crashed into the moon after transmitting thousands of clear, close-up pictures of the moon which were shown live on public television during the flight. Cosmonaut Leonov left his spacecraft while it was circling in orbit about the earth at 17,500 miles per hour, and floated at the end of a safety line, the first man to do somersaults in space; astronaut White actually maneuvered in space. Russian and American preparations for human visits to the moon gained momentum, the Russians launching a three-man craft and an American astronaut flying his ship into changes of orbit under his own control.

Some other events were: the discovery of warmer spots on the moon, 10°F to 86°F warmer than their surroundings (although still far below zero); the detection of reddish eruptions on the moon that may confirm the presence of volcanic action; the finding of water vapor on Venus and hydrogen on Saturn; the continued study of powerful magnetic fields in space; the possible discovery of biological forms in meteorites; the more accurate measurement of astronomical distances (2.2 million light-years to the Andromeda galaxy); the investigation of the solar wind, a huge arm of plasma containing charged particles that is hurled out of the sun and carries an extension of the sun's magnetism with it; the observation that comets seem to have the same types of carbon and in the same proportion as the earth, suggesting a common origin or the possibility that comets are leftover materials not needed when the planets were formed; and the further study of cool, dark, invisible stars, the presence of which is made known by their gravitational influence on nearby bright stars (they cause the bright stars to wobble slightly in their movement).

No list of recent developments could possibly be complete. Even if it were as exhaustive as man could make it, it would already be out of date before the last period is printed.